MUSIC THERAPY:
A FIELDWORK PRIMER

RONALD M.
BORCZON

Barcelona PUBLISHERS

Copyright © 2004 by Barcelona Publishers

ISBN 1-891278-21-5

2 4 6 8 9 7 5 3 1

Distributed throughout the world by:
Barcelona Publishers
4 White Brook Road
Gilsum NH 03448
Tel: 603-357-0236 Fax: 603-357-2073
Website: www.barcelonapublishers.com
SAN 298-6299

Cover illustration and design:
© 2004 Frank McShane

DEDICATION

Dedicated to the memory of my step-father

Stanley Macieukiewicz

TABLE OF CONTENTS

ACKNOWLEDGEMENTS

In writing this text I have drawn greatly from my own experience. On the morning of this particular writing I am two months away from celebrating 25 years as a music therapist. Who I have become as a person, musician, and music therapist would not be possible without having shared experiences with other people who in their own unique ways have helped me become who I am today. These people come to mind at different times as I write and my desire to acknowledge them is seated in a place of great gratitude accompanied by the feeling of being fortunate to have such friends, colleagues, teachers, and family.

I am grateful to God – for showing me the path and never failing when I stumble.

The guitar has been my other voice and so to my teachers: Bruce Holzman for just being Bruce; Madelyn Trible for pushing me beyond the limits of the guitar; and to Eliot Fisk – who demystified Bach for me so I could enjoy him even more.

To the friends who know me so well and still choose to be my friend: Gino Ferrare, Tas Steves, Frank and Diana Tomlinson, Steve Thachuk, Bill Arey, Don Seelinger, Jim Dziwak and John DiAquino. My FSU forever guitar geek buddies: Michael Chapdelaine, Steve Robinson, and Adam Holzman.

The CSUN Music Therapy and Wellness Clinic staff: Julie Berghofer, Holly Baxter, Lesa MacEwan, Kasi Peters, and Penny Roberts. You are the brightest and the best. Your clinical skills continue to amaze me, but then I realize that these skills are just an offshoot of who you are… and I am amazed even more. To those at California State University, Northridge who have supported the cause of music therapy: Jerry Leudders, Ron Purcell, Bill Toutant and David Aks.

To my cousins Norrie Dunsmore and Sue Kazlauskas – you are the best cousins in the whole world.

To my mom, the strongest survivor I know. To my sister Gloria – a shining light in a world that could use more. Sisters like you have special corners in heaven just waiting for them. To my brother Norm, there are no words to describe how much you mean to me.

To my favorite youngest daughter Molly, who asked me last night what it was like to write a book, and then said, "That is, after all, what I will be doing someday." My reply was, "It's hard." To my favorite middle daughter Claire, who has the heart of an angel. And to my favorite oldest daughter Jordyn, the "leader of the pack."

To Karen who gives hope to all women that you can indeed help a man to change … but not that much.

To the two most influential music therapy educators in my life, Ken Bruscia and Jayne Standley. You both encouraged me in my career and you both have been consummate role models. Your impact on me is passed on to my students, and most importantly, to my clients.

To Becky Olivera, an Art Therapist who hired me in my first full time job working in a psychiatric hospital. You were a great boss – demanding excellence from your staff. I learned a great deal from you back then. To Carolyn Braddock, an amazing therapist and even more amazing friend. To Cheryl Dileo and Darlene Brooks, friends till the end.

A special thanks to Rachel Gerstein for reading this and helping it to become a better text.

To my students who have inspired much of this text. May you all touch the lives of your clients with your gifts.

And finally, to my racquetball buddies, Mike Fister, Ron Carmona, Frank Saraceno, Ernst Aschacher , Dan Woelfel, and Bob Lenart – you guys are friends on and off the court. Thanks for your friendship all these years.

INTRODUCTION

I can still remember the first time I was alone and working with a client in an actual music therapy session. I had a different feeling than when I volunteered and my role was just to be a helper. Now, I was supposed to know what I was doing, I was the one with the knowledge to help the client progress in the therapy session. My heart was racing, I am certain that my breath was short, and a general sense of nervousness and anxiety was in my body. After all, this was my chosen profession, and if I did not do well what would that say about ME? I then thought, "I should not be feeling this way: I have the greatest teachers in the world, I have watched dozens of videotapes of what to do, I have my session outline completely memorized and there is a smile plastered on my face. What could possibly go wrong?"

What I was experiencing is what most beginning therapists experience no matter what the discipline: Pre-Session Operational Anxiety (PSOA). This particular diagnosis will not be found in any book as a clinical disorder, but I am certain that it exists in the majority of the population called, "The Novice (inexperienced) Therapist." To think that this diagnosis is owned only by the music therapy student is a fallacy. I have spoken to many students and young professionals of various disciplines and this thing I call PSOA is very common. It is a universal emotional consequence of wanting to be in the helping profession, yet not having enough experience to truly feel confident. I do believe, however, that since we use music more than words in our specific modality of music therapy, and because at the core we are artists/musicians, we can feel this anxiety more intensely than those who rely on verbal techniques. Additionally, as students, we read and learn about the power of a music therapy session and this, combined with our own musical nature, may increase the intensity of our anxiety level in our first sessions.

We are musicians and are trained to memorize music through cognitive associations, motor behaviors, practice techniques and repetition in order to physically play/sing the notes. We use our emotional being (soul) to play these notes that have been drilled into our body and brains in order to have an emotional impact on other human beings. We are also taught that mistakes are bad. I was watching the Ken Burns chronicle of Baseball on PBS and in the first segment he stated that if a batter fails 7 out of 10 times at bat he is considered great. I was struck both by the way he worded this statistic and by the truth that was contained in this sentence. Now, comparing music to baseball is not really fair; but if we did, can you imagine missing 70% of your notes and having a good performance? So mistakes, if viewed from a different perspective, might indicate how good you are or can become. I am not advocating that mistakes are OK, or should go on indefinitely, but the novice music therapist is often in fear of making mistakes as he/she goes into the therapy session. The fear of making mistakes will impede the basic skills of the therapist and will take away the sense of truly being present with the client. Later in the book I will talk about "doing no harm." Mistakes that "do no harm" are events that might actually expedite a process in some cases. What remains, however, is that the fear of making a mistake can be the biggest mistake.

> Stay open to challenges -
> they lead to growth.

Throughout this book I will present concepts, practical strategies, and information that will help you develop as a music therapist. Strategies intended to help you sidestep potential problems will be given along with reality-based interventions and skills. The best way to maturation, however, is through practical experience, and this handbook will help you in your development of that experience.

The term "process" is an important aspect of any therapy or theoretical orientation. It means that through time, self-investigation, emotional, cognitive, behavioral and sometimes spiritual growth, maturation towards a goal is realized and eventually the goal is accomplished. To become a good music therapist, you must go through a process. Even if you are a returning student with a great deal of life experience, you must recognize that this is a process and be open to it.

You should to be open to:

- Expanding who you are with various populations and who you are becoming as a music therapist.
- Learning how music is utilized with diverse populations. This learning can never stop (even if you think you already know it all).
- Learning helping skills along with your musical skills. It is the blend of these two areas that help define you as a music therapist. It is the process of developing the helping skills that is the major focus of this handbook.
- Growing as a person. Your own personal growth is one of the most important aspects of being a good therapist. Being congruent in your thoughts, feelings and behaviors is a lifelong goal and daily pursuit.

Areas will be addressed throughout the primer that can reassure you that you are not alone in your growth. I hope these areas will help you through your practicum, internship, and early professional career. This is intended as a roadmap to help you on you journey towards becoming a good music therapist. As with most any roadmap, there are many things not listed on it that you may encounter as you progress to your final destination. With this in mind, use it as a guide, not as a doctrine.

MUSIC THERAPY:

A FIELDWORK PRIMER

Chapter 1

ATTRIBUTES OF A MUSIC THERAPIST

WHY ARE YOU IN MUSIC THERAPY?

When I interview incoming students I ask them why they want to become a music therapist. They often stumble over this question and come up with an answer that eventually revolves around helping people and their own general experience in music. Once in awhile there is a student who opens up and shares his/her experience with the power of music in his/her own life. This conversation usually takes one of two directions. One direction is when I get the sense that the student is unconsciously seeking entrance to this program to get his/her own issues worked out; the other direction is when the student has gone through a process (possibly involving personal therapy) and is coming into this interview with a mature viewpoint on why he/she is in the profession. There will probably be a difference between these two students in their educational careers as one is working more on his/her own issues and the other is learning how to help others work on theirs. Therefore, having a clear understanding of why you're in the field of music therapy is the first step in becoming a good music therapist. If this understanding is absent, you are on a path without a personal foundation for this profession. You need to know why this is a calling for you, and it is usually more than the "I want to help people" answer. In working with this word "help," Bruscia, in *Defining Music Therapy* (1998) states:

> "The therapist is someone who makes a commitment to help another person, and to be available (as necessary and appropriate) whenever the person needs or seeks that help. Thus, a therapist is, by definition, the person who provides the help, and the client is the person who receives the help. While this seems blatantly obvious, there is something implied in this statement which needs to be said nevertheless. What makes the

helping relationship in therapy a unique one, is that it is neither mutual nor reciprocal. That is, it is the therapist's responsibility to help the client - it is not the client's responsibility to help the therapist in return." (p.47)

Another type of response when asked why one wants to go into Music therapy is this: "I need something to fall back on if I can't make it as a _____ (performer, song writer, band member, etc). This is the most disturbing answer of all because it implies that the student has not really thought about or investigated the field. The student is not aware of the self-discipline required for this work and will not be prepared for the amount of time, effort, and study that is associated with the discipline. Most of these students generally drop the concept of being a music therapist early in the program.

> Be clear in your understanding
> as to why you are entering
> the field of music therapy.

QUALITIES DEFINED BY THE AMERICAN MUSIC THERAPY ASSOCIATION

This profession is grounded in personal qualities, musical abilities and in the art of music. In looking at what personal attributes make up a good music therapist, the American Music Therapy Association (AMTA) website (2002) states:

"Personal Qualifications of a music therapist include a genuine interest in people and a desire to help others empower themselves. The essence of music therapy practice involves establishing caring and professional relationships with people of all ages and abilities. Empathy, patience, creativity, imagination, openness to new ideas, and understanding of oneself are also important attributes. Because music therapists are musicians as well as therapists, a background in and love of music are also essential. Individuals considering a career in music therapy are advised to gain experience through volunteer opportunities or summer work in nursing homes, camps for children with disabilities, and other settings which serve the needs of people with disabilities."

This definition contains several salient points upon which I have elaborated below. As you read through these points, reflect upon your own qualities and skills.

Genuine Interest in People

In this description of the qualities of the music therapy, the idea of "helping others" is the first concept listed but it is coupled with a "genuine interest" and the idea that in helping others you are enabling them to eventually "help themselves." While it is true that the altruistic experience of helping others in need can enhance our own self worth, that is not the primary reason which underscores this concept. As stated earlier, this profession is about helping others, not for the primary purpose of feeling good about what we do. You should be comfortable with people in general before working with others who are in need. This genuine interest is something that is more innate than developed in the personality structure. While this does not necessarily mean that you need to be an extrovert, it is the underlying desire that is most important.

Caring and Professional

The next line indicates that you must be a "caring" person as implied in the context of "professional relationships." The idea being conveyed is that you need to understand the boundaries of Therapist-Client relationships. To "care" means to have concern for another. It can also mean providing assistance for another. Both of these meanings relate to being a music therapist. But there is a line that can be crossed professionally, ethically, and emotionally if in the process of "caring," the relationship of therapist-client is violated. Through the study of ethics in music therapy you begin to understand what to do when difficult situations arise that question the "Professional Relationship." The Code of Ethics for the music therapist is the underlying moral and certified guide to get you through what to do when professional relationships are in question. Referring to this document as well as to a mentor in music therapy (which will be discussed later in the book) will help you work through the difficult situations involving boundaries.

Empathy

One of the most difficult concepts for a young therapist to understand is that of empathy. Carl Rogers in *A Way of Being* (1980) defines it as follows:

> "It means entering the private world of the other and becoming thoroughly at home in it. It involves being sensitive, moment by moment, to the changing felt meanings which flow in this other person, to the fear or rage or tenderness or confusion or whatever he or she is experiencing. It means temporarily moving in the other's life, moving about in it delicately without making judgments." (p.142)

What this means is that as the client experiences, you are also in that state of "experiencing" yet remaining separate. A musical example of empathy is a client playing a melodic line while you are playing exactly the same melodic line with him/her an octave higher or lower. It is the same feeling yet separate. As the client changes modes from major to minor, you make that shift also. You remain "with" him/her – while remaining separate.

This might be a difficult concept to grasp especially when dealing with severely challenged children who may be nonverbal and impaired with various physical handicaps. But the application of this attribute might be most effective with these individuals. Having the ability to try to see the world as these children see the world, and experience the world as they experience the world, is a challenge. Yet in doing so you are bringing to them music, which may be the most powerful force in their lives. As the music bridges a physical distance through vibration, you are on the other side resonating with the child emotionally. For the client this is often where healing, learning, and/or reaching out begins. The attribute of empathy is extremely powerful for the client, and is enhanced even further when coupled with music.

> The music bridges a physical distance through vibration, and you are on the other side in resonance.

Patience

In reviewing many books about what it takes to be a good counselor, very few list this attribute. In looking at music therapy, the attribute of patience is listed and for good reason. When you can calmly tolerate confusion, inefficiency, and delay without complaint and you can persevere with the clients as they move through their process and development, you exhibit the attribute of patience. Depending on the client, change can often be a long and arduous process. It is said that patience is a virtue mainly because while being patient you might be pushed to your limits in being able to control your own frustration within the process. While it is a virtue it is also something that could possibly get in the way of the session. If the task is too difficult for the client and you are not identifying this impasse, your patience might actually be in the way of progress. Sometimes the greatest deal of patience needs to be for your own self and development. You must be careful in your learning, objective in your self-evaluations, and patient in your progress.

Creative

In any helping profession the therapist needs to be creative. Part of the creative aspect in music therapy is a constant development and revision of the musical experience. While you can have plans to follow for group sessions or individual interventions, these plans must be fluid. Within the music session you must be creative in being able to recognize the music of the client(s), their reactions, what they are attempting to say to you through their music, their verbal responses to music, and their physical responses throughout the session. If you feel free to move naturally in your thinking and in your music making while adapting to the responses of the client, you're moving in the realm of being creative. Being creative is a gift, yet it can be learned and enhanced. Through classroom practice in lab settings and through allowing yourself to explore (often as a child explores), you can enhance your innate creative ability. Without this ability the music therapist must rely on written and preformed plans of intervention that often, because of what is going on for the client that day, need to be revised during the actual intervention, thus not keeping the client's welfare and progress at the forefront of the session.

Imagination

Imagination is closely tied to creativity. Imagination is being able to form mental images of things or events that are not yet present. It is the creation of new ideas for a myriad of purposes. In music performance part of the training is to be able to look at written notes on the staff and to be able to imagine the sound in your mind. The sound is not actually a physical reality, but you can hear it in your mind. Often you will visualize with your eyes closed the movement of your fingers on piano keys, strings, or a variety of other instruments. You "imagine" in your mind's eye what the reality might be.

In music therapy, imagination can be used as a therapeutic tool by having the client imagine while listening to or playing music. As a music therapist, you might imagine how a new musical intervention with a client might occur, or your imagination may be put in place spontaneously in order to enhance the creative aspect of the music therapy session. Imagination is a powerful attribute. Although it is listed after creativity in these attributes, in reality it is closely tied to the creative process.

Openness to New Ideas

As you progress through the music therapy curriculum, fieldwork placements, internship, and early employment, you'll be introduced to many new concepts that can challenge you intellectually, emotionally, and spiritually. What you take from each experience and how you integrate it into your style and personality enables you to become a better music therapist. In order to take something from an experience you must first be open to the experience. When I work with clients who have never had music therapy before, I generally thank them at the end of the session for being open to the experience. After allowing yourself to become involved with the many levels (cognitive, physical, emotional, etc.) of a new experience, you can decide on its value. This is being open – having an unbiased view of a potential experience, then allowing yourself to engage in the experience so you can subjectively be immersed and then objectively review what has happened.

> Being open to new experiences
> can help you grow as a therapist.

Understanding Oneself

I began this chapter with a tale of two students. One student wanted to help other people yet unconsciously was entering the field in order to help himself/herself. The other student had learned that through the process of development as a person, there is a desire to be involved in music therapy with the purpose of helping others. Understanding oneself is a critical attribute. You have a dual responsibility for not only your professional growth but also for your personal growth. Without really knowing who you are and why you do the things you do, it is difficult to help someone else who has embarked on the journey. A parallel to this is in teaching musical instruments. It is difficult to teach piano at a high level unless you have experience playing at a high level. The focus here is on the "experience" of playing the piano, and in therapy, your self-knowledge and understanding will ultimately help your client. This is vital not only to your growth and abilities, but ultimately you owe it to your clients to undergo a process such as the one they are experiencing.

Love of Music

Before the AMTA description ends there is a statement about the love of music and being a musician. While I believe it is hard to correlate the relationship of musical ability and therapeutic ability, I do believe and have witnessed that the music aspect of music therapy appears to be of a higher quality when conducted by a well-rounded musician. It is only through years of observation and review of not only students who are studying the field, but also of professionals I've witnessed in the field, that I arrive at this conclusion. A strong background in piano, guitar, and voice is essential for any entering music therapist. Additionally, having knowledge of the various percussion instruments and how they are played is extremely useful. The ability to hear melodies and provide a harmonic background is essential with many populations. The ability to improvise within a musical framework as well using music in such a way as to depict non-musical themes (i.e. animals playing, people running, etc.) are involved in any improvisational approach. The better developed one is in the skills of music, the more tools one will have as a music therapist.

> In becoming a music therapist you are a musician first. Then the therapy skills develop.

Volunteer Work

In preparing to enter this field the last part of the qualification section given by AMTA talks about volunteer work, which is the giving of one's time to benefit others. The experience that you gain prior to entering the field of music therapy (as well as the volunteer work done while studying music therapy) is vital. Summer volunteer work and apprenticeship with music therapists will enhance your development and prepare you for your internship and professional world. It helps you define your comfort level without the pressure of doing it "for a grade." The altruistic attribute of helping others for no real personal gain is a trait that seems prevalent in most mature music therapists. It is a virtue that is part of a lifelong journey.

ADDITIONAL ATTRIBUTES

In addition to those listed by AMTA, the following categories came out of an exercise from the California State University, Northridge Music Therapy Program. Theater students were introduced at the end of a functional skills class and were asked to improvise various roles based upon disability areas. The music therapy student had to improvise a music therapy session with the theater student to attain an assigned goal for each disability area. At the end of each session the theater major critiqued the style of the music therapy student. The most common positive attributes cited in these exercises are listed below.

Affect

Your general appearance of face, clothing, and body language can have a great deal of impact on what the client experiences. This is especially true if the client is visually oriented. How your face looks to them is often a powerful non-verbal tool that many therapists seem to overlook. The way you smile, raise your eyebrows during questions or inquiries, and the way your mouth looks at rest are various areas that you should think about.

Generally speaking, your affect needs to be one of acceptance. Your eyes need to be focused on the client in a way that allows the client to find safety within them. You need to observe, be present within the session, and not stare. You need to smile when appropriate and have it be natural and not contrived. Your body language should signal to the client that you are comfortable within the session and with him/her. Crossing of arms and legs in a tight fashion should be avoided. Be comfortable and open.

As you interact musically with the client you need to apply these same principles as you play instruments. This can often become challenging if you are not comfortable with the musical medium in which you are currently involved. In this case, develop more experience with that musical intervention so that your concentration is not so focused on your own musical ability.

Different facilities and/or therapeutic environments may require dress codes that you must adhere to. Make sure that you know what the standard is. Once you know the standard, become comfortable within that context. If you are uncomfortable with your dress, it adds another distraction. Whatever the dress code is, be comfortable and, above all, be professional in the selection of your wardrobe in adherence to the standard set by the employing agency.

The overall concept of affect is this: you should have an appearance that is inviting for the client. "Inviting" also means that the client perceives you as being trustworthy, caring, accepting, intelligent and professional. This perception by the client is most often made at an unconscious level. But make no mistake about it, this perception is formulated and processed into some aspect of awareness by the client.

Gentleness

Gentleness refers to a natural disposition that one might also think of as "kind." It also can encompass the concept of being serene, but not without energy. This sense of gentleness is exhibited in the manner of how you speak and appear. Your interactions should be the opposite of what you might consider harsh. If gentleness could be considered a musical term, it might fall into two categories: articulation and timbre. The articulation aspect of gentleness relates to how you speak and the timbre aspect relates to how you appear. These are wonderful qualities to nourish as you develop your skills.

Reinforcing

When I talk about reinforcing, I do not want it to be confused with verbal praise after each correct behavior, falling under the general category of Positive Reinforcement. Reinforcing may indeed have Positive Reinforcement as part of it, but this concept is larger than the technique. Reinforcing is a way of being, a sense of optimism that the client will progress through the treatment toward some goal. It is a posture of acknowledgement through which the client can sense a genuine positive caring about what the client is thinking, doing, or feeling at a given time. In this way it is truly "valuing" the client. Through the sense of reinforcement/acknowledgement, the client will have the desire to continue and work with the therapist because the therapist cares. It is not contrived, it is not a systematic way of operating, but it is truly a way of being.

I think that one can never truly be too reinforcing or optimistic about outcomes as long as it is coupled with a sense of reality. Some people are naturals at this. Others might need to recognize this is lacking and make a shift in cognition and behavior so that as they "do" they can "become." I think that noticing the best in people and situations is a key to this style and that practicing it often in daily life can increase your personal attributes as well as bring joy to those around you.

> Music therapy is a powerful and
> effective mechanism that brings you and
> the client together for the sole purpose
> of helping the client.

Reinforcing also has to do with faith in the process of music therapy. Faith entails four areas: First, faith in yourself that you are going to do the best you can considering where you are in your training, to be the helper with the aid of music. Second, faith that the client will have an experience that will at some level move him/her toward a therapeutic goal. Third, faith in the client as a human being and their innate possibility for growth. And fourth, faith in the concept that music therapy is a powerful and effective mechanism that brings you and the client together for the sole purpose of helping the client.

Quick Thinking

Being able to think quickly on your feet is an asset in most any job. In music therapy it often involves stopping a mallet from being thrown or an instrument from being damaged. In many cases it involves recognizing that something disastrous may be about to happen, and by your quick action a potential disaster may be avoided. By being aware of a client's potential for destructive behavior, you can be cautiously aware of dangerous situations in the making. Conversely, quick thinking applies to when the client does something positive and you are there to recognize and acknowledge this behavior in a manner that the client will understand. This recognition gains its power only if the recognition itself is important to the client.

Quick thinking can be learned as you gain experience. Learning warning signs is not so much population specific as it is client specific. Often an event occurs and you need to assimilate the ways in which the event manifested itself. By understanding the antecedents of behavior, you can intercede when necessary. The antecedents are often fast in the making, and therefore the thinking and action must be quick. If you are video taping the session, antecedents can be more easily recognized in the review of the videotape. This can be a valuable asset in managing behavior.

Creative quick thinking is a more positive look at this category. The ability to take what the client does and incorporate it into the activity is an example of creative thinking. I often imagine the entire being of a client as being a musical event. The client presents a series of sounds, sentences, or movements that can become the basis of a musical interaction. You can look at the rhythm of the movement or gesture, and match it on an instrument. You can take the pitch levels of words or vocalizations and create music from them or connect with them via your vocal response. If someone is speaking in sentences there is the flow of the sentence as well as the melodic inflections to work with. Creativity within the musical moment is a valuable asset that can be developed in your style.

Don't Entertain, Interact

At times clients wish to be entertained, and music therapists need to entertain and thus at times we oblige them. While putting on a show might be a technique, it can also become a pitfall. When the attention shifts from the client to you, is therapy really occurring? If you think it is occurring, who is really benefiting? There are always strategies to get the attention off of you and onto the client. It is simply a matter of first realizing that the session is becoming about you, and then cognitively shifting the focus to the client. You then alter your approach so that once again you are the helper and not the one being helped.

Interacting means that there is some evidence within the music therapy session that the client is participating in the session with you. You might be playing music together, drawing to music, talking about the music, etc. Listening can be considered interactive if it is purposeful in nature and part of the technique of the session. The result of this awareness will lie in the movement by the client into the music therapy session in such a way that the client's role can be worked with and expanded. Finally, the interaction may be entertaining as it holds the attention of the client, but if it becomes a performance that's all about you, something has gone awry.

Don't Break When in Difficult Situations

Music has the power to touch the emotional core of the human spirit. As it does, emotions can range from ecstatic joy to the depths of sorrow. Many times we can be caught off guard if we are not aware that the client may react in these extremes. There may come a time when events occur during the session where you may not know what to do. The experience in the session may then become "difficult" to handle. These events can involve a wide range of occurrences. For example, a child might tantrum and lose control, an adult might break down and start sobbing, or there may just be a long period of silence when it becomes very uncomfortable. It is key to note that many therapists have this experience. What becomes important is how you keep your composure, what you do for the client, and what you learn from the experience.

> There are times when the client needs to
> simply experience your
> presence and acceptance.

How you contain your reactions to various situations is critical. "Staying calm in the face of adversity" is not just a saying, it is also a strategy. Keeping your poise can be difficult at times, but it can be done. Sometimes you need to be able to remove yourself from the situation and objectively see what is happening as if you're watching from above. This is often the first step to take when a difficult situation arises. You must assess then whether there's any potential danger to yourself or the client. If there is danger there are steps you must take to keep both of you from harm. Many facilities have mandatory training seminars on how to best handle various types of dangerous situations. These steps need to be followed at this time. If there is no danger, you may try to be more empathetic with the client in order to understand why they are engaging in the current behaviors or feeling the current emotions.

Not every difficult situation will call for an intervention. In dealing with the client's feelings, it may not be appropriate to try to have the client change how he/she is feeling. Always think before you speak in these situations. There are times when the client does not need to hear any words but instead needs to experience your presence, not a presence of fear or anxiety, but a presence of acceptance. Possibly, it might be appropriate to improvise or accompany in some way a musical response that will help the client through the present difficulty. If words are needed, however, choose them carefully. If the therapeutic direction of the session indicates a redirection of behavior, be specific in the stating of the behavior so that there is no confusion as to what is being addressed. If you're looking for words of comfort try not to use "everything is going to be okay" as at that moment things may not feel okay and the client may not be prepared to hear this. Later in the book I will go over various phrases of intervention that can be used when music brings up emotions that need to be discussed.

Learning from these complicated events is important to your development. After a difficult session, reflect upon your composure, intervention and overall performance. Realize that you have survived this difficult situation and take what you can from it. Because of this event, you are different person and a different therapist from the one you were when you entered that session. If the results of the session were not what you had hoped, realize that you have made it through this and learn from the experience. Later in the book, "What We Learn From Our Clients" will be discussed. Many times you need to recognize what it is that the client has just taught you about being a music therapist. Even though we are the helpers, what we learn in a post-session review teaches us how to be better music therapists. This kind reflection may become your greatest learning asset as you grow in your skills and style.

Intellectually Aware

It is essential to be able to understand the wide variety of theories and learn the strategies of music therapy. The ability to remember concepts and strategies and then draw upon them within the context of the music therapy session is crucial. It is not enough to be able to understand the theory and then be able to do well when tested on the theory. You must be able to apply these concepts in real clinical situations.

There are cultural differences in clients, and awareness and sensitivity to these are needed. Understanding cultural diversity and cultural dynamics is important and helps in the development of your connection with the client. Becoming familiar with the music of the client's culture is often a link for you and the client. From here the relationship can develop.

Intellectual awareness also refers to the thinking process while in the session. I often notice that students don't take enough time to think about what they're doing while involved within a client. I'll often instruct them to consciously think at least three times during the session to stop and observe what is going on, as if they had stepped out of themselves. They need to see how the client is behaving at that moment and how they are reacting to what the client is doing. When I do this, I will often ask myself this question: "What is this client trying to tell me right now?" This is a very important exercise and process. It is through moments like these that you can really assess what is going on and what direction you should be taking.

> I will often ask myself this question:
> "What is the client trying to
> tell me right now?"

Hard Working

I don't think that I have ever met a successful music therapist who did not have and employ this attribute. From the beginning, just being a music student is hard work. The music degree is not an easy prize to achieve. Coupled with therapy, it involves entirely new challenges. Once out of school, employment and development of the job can be arduous. To put it simply, it is not a job for the weary or faint of heart. You must have physical and emotional stamina, and these are manifested individually in various ways. Ultimately, it is healthy to view the hard work as a set of lifelong opportunities for growth. If not, you can become burnt out and possibly bitter. Keep it all in perspective, taking one day at a time, but still work hard.

SUMMARY

The many attributes that have been listed in this chapter are often considered the minimum for being in this profession. The AMTA lists many of the qualities that an aspiring music therapist should already have or should be in the process of developing. Some of these characteristics are inborn or come naturally to some, while others need development. Through the education of the music therapist, many of these areas are addressed. A careful and objective self-evaluation of your own attributes should be done. In areas of weakness, devise a plan to develop these areas so that they can be equal to your strengths. The plan itself can be creative in nature, but it is also helpful to have a mentor or a teacher to develop this with you. It is then your continued responsibility to be proactive in the initiation of the plan.

Education does not stop once the degree is achieved. After graduation the exam for becoming a board certified music therapist should be taken and, once passed, continuing education is needed to maintain this level. Seeking out and participating in continuing education possibilities in areas outside music therapy can be very helpful depending on your area of expertise. You can ask colleagues to keep you informed of conferences and lectures that are pertinent to their areas of expertise. You can investigate other professional organizations with which you share some interests and learn about the types of professional development they offer. A good rule to keep in mind when going this route is: As you learn more, how will it make your music therapy session more meaningful for your client. Being creative in the application of your new knowledge will benefit your music therapy practice.

Understanding the motivating factors as to why a client engages in behaviors is an important aspect of any therapy. Understanding why you do the things you do is even more important. Without this understanding, you are doing a disservice to your clients. Not everyone is appropriate for this field (even if you think you are). If you don't really know why you have chosen this course, you have taken a step in the wrong direction.

Your potential in life is limited only by what you perceive your potential to be. Having a realistic grasp on this concept is the key to becoming an effective music therapist. The operative words are "realistic grasp." When working on a treatment team, the team evaluates all areas of a client and comes to a conclusion as to what goals are appropriate and realistic for the client (in some instances, depending on the situation, the client has input in this process). These goals are set so that the achievement of them can be accomplished. They are objective and measured. Your success as a music therapist can be thought of in a similar fashion. This chapter gives you a list of attributes that can be thought of as goals. It is ultimately up to you to evaluate your strengths and weaknesses as you embark on your course of personal development.

REFERENCES

American Music Therapy Association Website (2002).
   http://www.musictherapy.org
Bruscia, K. (1998). *Defining music therapy (2nd Ed.)*. Gilsum, NH:
   Barcelona Publishers.
Rogers, C. (1980). *A way of being.* Boston, MA: Houghton Mifflin:
Truax, C.B. and Carkhuff, R. (1964). The old and the new: theory and
   research in counseling and psychotherapy. *Personality and
   Guidance Journal.* 42, p. 860-866.

Chapter 2

THE FIRST ENCOUNTER

You are about to embark on your first session and there are aspects of preparation to be addressed. Proper preparation is an asset in any endeavor and it is no different in the field of music therapy. There will be a multitude of feelings and thoughts that you will be going through. What follows is a description of areas that may help you in having a successful first encounter (and may possibly be useful for subsequent sessions) in your clinical work.

DO YOUR HOMEWORK

In the last chapter this concept was introduced as it related to getting information about the client and facility in order to help alleviate your anxiety level. Expanding on this will help you in your overall preparation for your work.

Know as much as you can about the setting where you will be working. If possible take a tour of the facility and get to know your contact person, who will often be your supervisor. Know how long it takes to get to the setting. Leave yourself plenty of time in case there is something unforeseen that occurs on your way. Understand what the dress code is and be sure to follow it. Look at the room where you will be doing your sessions. Find out where to go if there is an emergency while in the session as well as out of a session. I usually use the rule of thumb that I would be the closest to the door in case of any emergency. In some cases, when the client tends to wander or run away, the therapist may be best located between the client and the door.

In regards to equipment, find out what equipment will be available to you. Is there a piano available? What instruments are on hand and is there a stereo? Will you need additional time for setup? Note the condition of the instruments and equipment.

> Keep yourself between
> the client and the door.

In preparation for meeting the client remember that there are generally three reasons why someone is need of treatment. These are easily categorized by a condition of being OK or not OK.

- The client feels that he/she is not OK. The client may appear to be working well in society, yet there is something that is going on that is causing enough distress that he/she feels intervention is needed. The client may also be in a place where daily life is being so affected by their problems that they notice intervention is needed and he/she seeks help.
- The family says he/she is not OK. The family structure may notice that there are things going on with the client that are not within the realm of what the family considers normal. If a child is not attending to visual cues at a young age, the family may have the child assessed for a visual disability. A female teenager may begin to lose a great deal of weight and stop eating and is caught lying about her food intake and the family becomes concerned and intervenes. The family, if functioning normally, will serve as its own barometer and can take action within itself.
- The society says that the client is not OK. In some cases when the family does not notice a problem, or is unavailable, and the client is unaware that there is an issue, society steps in and intervenes. The *Diagnostic and Statistical Manual of Mental Disorders-Text Revision* (DSM-IV-TR) is a comprehensive book devoted to the classification of psychiatric illness. Within it there are lists of diagnostic behaviors that are deemed outside the limits of what society deems normal. If a person is beginning to talk to himself/herself on the job, or is seen talking to someone in the corner of the room that is not really there (hallucination), the society of the work place may intervene in order to get the client help.

> Three reasons why a
> person is in treatment:
> the client feels he/she is not OK;
> the family feels that he/she is not OK;
> society feels he/she is not OK.

To know why your client is in treatment is important. Initially you should ask for information from the supervisor or others that may have worked with this client. To know as much as you can about the general characteristics of their diagnosis is imperative. Conduct your own research via the Internet, library, and textbooks so that at the moment of interaction with the client you have a better understanding of the person in front of you. If they have a specific syndrome, for example Williams Syndrome, you need to be familiar with the pertinent characteristics. You should also know whether the client is on medication and if so, any side effects of that medication, as it may have an impact on the performance level of the client.

ROLES

There are many different ways in which first experiences might be arranged. In any experience there are different roles that you may play. According to the music therapist, or the setting, your role may be defined as observer, participant, co-leader, or leader. These may have some crossover once the session has begun and are not always mutually exclusive.

As an Observer:

- Ask the music therapist if you can aid in the preparation for the session. Help gather appropriate materials and with set up.
- Make sure you understand the session format and the goals.
- Notice the therapist's methods of interaction and technique.
- Be cognizant of how the music is being used.
- Know what the objectives are and see if and how they are met through the musical intervention.
- Note the clients' responses, reactions, participation level, behaviors, symptoms, and interaction with the music.
- As you have done your homework on the client, be aware of their pathology coming through in the session.
- Ask the music therapist whether there is anything specific that you should watch for.
- Be aware of the flow of the session – the feeling of a beginning, middle, and end.

As a Participant:

- Make sure you understand the directives of your supervisor.
- Your participation should set an example as you are often serving as a role model for clients who can learn from your actions.
- Remember that this is still a session for the client. There are times when your own issues might surface in the session and you need to keep those in check. If necessary, process these with the music therapist after the session has concluded.
- Assume a supportive role with the clients. Do not force them to do anything but try to increase their involvement by encouraging, motivating, restating directions, or assisting where necessary or when requested by the music therapist.
- Be aware of any cues the music therapist might give you to change roles and be more of a co-leader/helper if needed.

As a Co-leader or Leader:

- Be alert to the client's reactions and needs as they present themselves in sessions.
- Do not isolate yourself with other students or staff. You should be relating primarily to clients during sessions.
- Be careful not to pay an inordinate amount of attention to some clients while ignoring others.
- If more than one leader is present during the session, spread yourselves out among the clients.
- Be consistent and courteous with clients.
- Try to be understanding, yet avoid emotional involvement.
- Attempt to communicate with them as honestly and directly as possible, but use discretion in revealing personal information.
- Do not probe into their problems or attempt to analyze (in the early sessions you may not have the knowledge or experience necessary to process the information).
- Avoid making value judgments.
- Focus on the client's assets, abilities, and strengths whenever possible.
- Give proper acknowledgement and reinforcement when appropriate.
- Do not reinforce the client's inappropriate behavior, or any skepticism they may express with regard to treatment or the facility.
- Save all your questions concerning the session proceedings, client's involvement, reactions, client care, etc. for after the session.

After the Session:

- If at any time problems arose and you were unsure as to how they should be handled, consult with the music therapist.
- Report to the supervisor any significant patient behavior you have observed.

- Aid the music therapist with cleanup and proper maintenance of the instruments and materials. Report any needed repairs or depleted supplies.
- Document in an approved format (for example, journaling) all sessions that you have taken part in. Aside from aiding in your assimilation of skills in the therapeutic use of music, a thoughtful write-up can aid the music therapist by presenting a fresh outlook on possibilities for session variations or change. A good write-up can also help the music therapist to focus in on your needs and interests as a maturing therapist.
- Process the events of the session with the music therapist supervisor.

YOU WILL SURVIVE

I think that it is safe to say all music therapists have had the experience of playing an end-of-semester jury (or review) on their instrument. The anxiety that one feels in this situation is hard to describe, yet nonetheless is ever present. For many of us our feelings of self worth seem to be on the line in this situation. Wanting to get a good grade is just part of it, but music is extremely personal and on some level we feel defined by the notes we play and the expression of those notes. When walking into a jury, a recital, or specific types of performances, the need to be perfect - perhaps accepted and validated - is running through our thoughts and feelings, if not consciously, then surely at the unconscious level. These thoughts can often get in the way of a well-prepared recital or jury and events may not go as planned. The subsequent feeling of disappointment and/or failure can be overwhelming. Yet there is always one thing that is certain when this performance is over: You have survived it. You are breathing, walking, talking and feeling... you made it through the event!

We all have learned well the art of being anxious. It is part of who we are as humans and is handed down to us through our collective ancestors. It is easy to have the switch activated, especially when you are meeting a client for the first time or entering a new clinical situation. There are ways to alleviate some of these feelings such as knowing the population by doing volunteer work, adequately preparing for the situation by researching the type of client(s) served, having a strong sense of who you are and realizing that the client may also be nervous about meeting someone new. This last realization may help you keep this in focus - this is all about the client, and not about you. It is OK to check in with yourself to see how you are doing through a session, but then you must get right back on track and focus on the client and their needs.

> Therapy is always about the client, not
> the therapist.

If you don't know already, there are many ways of doing things. To a musician who is trained in the technical application of physical movements to get a desired sound, this statement of "many ways" might be difficult to grasp. Music teachers often feel that they have a patent on the proper technique for playing an instrument, or the best and only way of performing certain musical phrases. In therapy there are guidelines to be observed, and you will learn them. But when you create anxiety in yourself by trying to do the one and only right thing for the client, it is often an impossible task. What you do as a music therapist will often depend on what the client needs from moment to moment. While playing an instrument a teacher might give you clues as to what to do when things are not going well in a piece or if you should have a memory lapse. In therapy things can also unravel. If things are not going a certain way and you begin to panic it might be helpful to:

- Notice your breath - catch your breath if you are in a pattern of a shortness of breath, and then breathe deeply.
- Become objective about what is going on - remove your emotional self-judgment.
- Ask yourself, "What does this client need right now?" Then do what is necessary.
- If you are unsure of the previous answer, keep observing in an objective fashion and find the solution.

- Follow your instincts – those innate abilities that have gotten you this far. Trust in what you already know.

At the end of this process, one thing will surely be true: You will have survived the session and most likely, your client will have survived it too!

YOUR CLIENT WILL SURVIVE

So now that it is established that you will make it through the session, how about your client? Clients have an amazing ability to persevere and move through adversity. By the virtue of now being *your* client, he/she will already most likely have survived trauma, trouble, adversity, illness, and possibly prejudice. Meeting you is not the worst thing that could or should happen.

In helping the client survive a music therapy session, the rule of "Do No Harm" needs to be stated. You have an ethical responsibility not to harm the client physically or emotionally. Your obligation to keep him/her safe is paramount. Physical harm is initially what comes to mind when one thinks of being "harmful," but emotional harm can be done when you initiate musical activities that are beyond your scope of training. Therefore, know your limitations, stay in your comfort area of leadership and therapeutic style. As you grow in experience and education, your maturity as a music therapist develops, but always keep in mind your comfort level of clinical intervention.

If your career as a music therapist is beginning to take shape, and you are developing and gaining knowledge through your varied experiences, then not only will you survive the session, your client will too.

therapist and client is no different. It all begins for the client in the first session. For you, however, the relationship has begun prior to the first meeting as you have done your homework and gathered information about the client. The client, on the other hand, is coming into this first session not really knowing who you are and in many cases not having ever experienced a music therapy session. The first thing you want to do is to introduce yourself by saying your name, who you are ("I'm the music therapist who will be working here today"; "I'm the music therapy student from the local university"), and possibly give a brief overview of what will be going on that day. In many cases you will know the client's name and you may want to use it in your opening introduction: "Hi Ray, my name is Betty and I am a music therapist (music therapy student) from International University. I have been looking forward to meeting you." Some clients may not know what music therapy is and communicate a desire to know a little about it. Be prepared to briefly describe music therapy in easily understandable terms and maybe share why you're there to do music therapy.

> Introduce yourself.
> Say who you are (music therapist or
> music therapy student, etc.).
> Explain music therapy in simple
> language (if this is needed).
> Give a brief overview of what might be
> occurring in the session.

As the session begins become aware of your listening skills. As a musician your training in aural perception has primarily involved the understanding of harmony and intervals. As a music therapist, your listening skills must go beyond just a musical understanding. Notice tension and resolution in words, phrases, and in body movements. Be attuned to the rhythm of the voice, sentence structure, and body language. Think of the client as a piece of music that is constantly flowing and changing in time. Your role is to help this symphonic outline embodied in human form discover meaning and health through their music. Overall, be aware of what the client is telling you verbally, musically, and through body language.

> Do not get emotionally involved in a
> reaction from a client at any level,
> rather be an observer of the response
> and attempt to find meaning
> in the response.

First sessions are often an assessment time to get to know more about the client. While it is good to have a plan for your first session, allowing the client to share the lead can help in the development of trust. This of course will vary from population to population, and the goals of the client are always priorities. Thus, it may not be appropriate to let the client have a leadership role, but where this technique can be utilized, it can also help in the development of a trusting relationship between music therapist and client, especially in the early stages of the relationship.

One of the most important things to remember in your first session (as well as in your journey as a professional music therapist) is that every reaction or response from the client to the music is considered a valid response. This response gives you information about the client and how they view the world. Far too often if the client reacts in such a way as to be labeled "negative," a less experienced therapist may take this personally as a reaction towards himself/herself. With this in mind, do not be emotionally reactive to this type of response from the client, but rather be an observer of this response and attempt to find meaning within the response. In this way you are accepting the client. You are giving the client freedom to react and respond to the musical intervention without judgment. This unbiased response from you will be perceived by the client on many different levels and will help in the development of trust in the relationship. You'll also begin to understand the way the client communicates with the world. Being able to communicate with the client at the client's level is a basic tenet of success in the therapeutic relationship. The groundwork for a successful relationship begins when you walk through the door and greet the client.

> Give the client freedom to interact, react, and respond to the musical intervention.

SUMMARY

This chapter delves into what to do prior to, and during the first session. Being prepared by knowing as much as you can about the client and the facility will help alleviate initial anxious feelings to some extent, but to be somewhat apprehensive as you enter the session is normal.

Be clear about what your role is in the session. If you are not sure, ask the supervisor how you would best be utilized in the session. Whether you are observing the first session or actually conducting it, you will make a good first impression by being professional in your dress, prepared in your methodology, and knowledgeable in regard to the client's diagnosis.

How the client views the world often comes out in their response to the musical intervention. You must keep an objective (if they are not enjoying the activity – don't take it personally) and open mind to the responses of the client as they are valid and are giving you information about the client. While you should not at this point interpret meanings for the client, you should take note of your interpretation of their responses for your own understanding. Keep in mind your musical training. See your client as a musical being, with melody, harmony, form, rhythm, timbre and dynamics. Seeing the client in these terms can help you develop music therapy interventions that can help the client move into a more harmonious and structured state of being.

REFERENCES

Borczon, R.M. (1997). *Music Therapy: Group vignettes.* Gilsum, NH:
  Barcelona Publishers.
Rogers, C. (1980). *A way of being.* Boston, MA: Houghton Mifflin.
Martin, D. (1983). *Counseling and therapy skills.* Prospect Heights, Il:
  Waveland Press, Inc.

Chapter 3

WHAT WE LEARN FROM CLIENTS

While in the music therapy experience, you are working with, enabling, playing with, listening to, asking questions of, observing, reacting to, facilitating, and making mental notes of what is happening with and for the client. Your focus is primarily on what the client is saying musically, non-musically, verbally, and non-verbally. You are present with the client and experiencing empathy. You are checking in with yourself as to your own transference issues so that you can continue to be unbiased in your own reactions. Through reflecting on the experience via journal writing or supervision, you can begin to look at what you may have learned from your client. The process of learning from the client is reflective in nature and begins in the moments after the session has ended.

The following sections are drawn from class discussions specifically addressing this content area. Students, in a seminar format, were asked what they had learned from their clients in the session from the previous week. These headings will not pertain to each and every clinical setting. Some of them cross over many different populations such as the first one, "Expect the Unexpected," while "Certain Clients Can and Will Manipulate You," may be more appropriate to a psychiatric setting and not really seen in a hospice situation. Described below are the most commonly mentioned areas and are by no means all-inclusive.

EXPECT THE UNEXPECTED

Whenever a client has a reaction to the music that we are not anticipating, it is called "unexpected." In this case, letting your surprise come through is usually not appropriate for the moment. For example, a client, while listening to a beautiful Mozart concerto, says that it reminds him of a dream where there is war and carnage. Rather than showing your surprise at such a comment, it is better for you consider the following: 1) This is an aberrant reaction to something that most people view as beautiful - why then did it occur at all? 2) It has ignited something in the client that would warrant some initial verbal intervention and possibly lead to musical expression or listening exploration. Remember that the client who is involved in music therapy is there for a reason. Thus the client will have different views of the world and different ways of relating to the world as well as to the music. Unexpected events are a part of life, and in music therapy they may become - expected.

BE CAREFUL OF LABELLING

Labels are often derived from the diagnosis. Diagnosis is necessary to understand what kind of behavior pattern(s) is typically associated with the given name. They are useful in helping professionals find a common language through which to understand global conceptions of client behavior. The problem is that once a diagnosis is given, the client may lose his/her true sense of identity and become merely a label. A danger is also encountered when the client, because of the diagnosis, is expected (as in number one above) to behave a certain way. Because he/she behaves in a certain way the diagnosis in a sense becomes "earned," it does not mean that they are unable to move out of those behaviors from time to time.

PEOPLE DESIRE
ACKNOWLEDGEMENT

One of my favorite thoughts from reading about Transactional Analysis (Eric Berne) is that people will work for strokes. Positive or negative, it doesn't matter, they will just work for strokes. Here, a crossing of an ideological concept between Transactional Analysis and Behaviorism occurs. However, the concept serves the point that in many different theoretical postulations it is to be noted that people will engage in behaviors for a definite purpose, whether they know it or not. The purpose of the behavior stems from a desire, and in the desire for reinforcement and acknowledgement lies a great motivator for all types of behaviors. Some behaviors serve the person well, and some do not. In either case the person is often unaware of the reason for the behavior. He/she only knows that at the moment of reinforcement and/or acknowledgement, a need is met, which initially stems from a desire.

BE ACUTELY AWARE OF AGENDAS (BEHAVIOR IS PURPOSEFUL)

An agenda is something that a person holds close to oneself in order to have some sort of internal gain. It is a plan of action that is most likely covert, and is set into motion so that the person may achieve some sort of gratification from its successful outcome. It is almost always self-serving in nature. So how does a client utilize agendas? He/she puts them into motion to get what he/she wants, which often leads to a stroke for him/her. A problem arises when the stroke is perceived as something "good" by him/her alone, while it actually may be counterproductive for the client in the overall scheme of his/her life. If it is counterproductive, it will serve as mechanism for failure in therapy and the pattern of behavior that the client is engaged in will continue. For the therapist who gets caught up by the hidden agenda it is hard not to feel like a failure at its end. Agendas can be recognized initially by patterns of behavior that the client is involved in that, when the therapist intervenes, there is a sense of failure felt by the therapist. Agendas are used to trip you up, so when you feel like the intervention didn't work, ask yourself if you were set up so the session would fail. If the answer is "yes," begin to notice not only the client's patterns of behavior, but also how you are reacting to those behaviors.

KISS – (KEEP IT SIMPLE, STUDENTS)

Develop objectives at a level where the client feels a sense of accomplishment. Sometimes just being able to sing one note in pitch is enough. Sometimes just being able to sing a note that fluctuates in its pitch is enough. Sometimes just being able to make a sound is what the client needs. I think you understand where I am going with this: A behavior that may appear simple may actually be very complex.

When goals are given in treatment settings, they are broad-based in nature. From that goal the small objectives are developed that when strung together will lead to that goal. In keeping it simple, the objectives are the focus. They are to be attainable so that the client can recognize his/her successes and accomplishments. When you are thinking about earning a bachelors degree, your first step out of bed on the first day of classes is your first objective. Remember, first your pants, then your shoes.

MODIFY YOUR ACTIONS
TO CREATE TRUST AND SECURITY

The client, through trusting you and feeling secure, can enable you and the music therapy environment to foster growth. In order to have a trusting relationship between you and your client you must provide the structure that will allow for this to occur. How is this accomplished? With each client, approach him/her refreshed and new in each session. This means leaving behind whatever has happened with the previous client, and whatever is going on in your personal life outside that therapy room. With this accomplished, you can be free to meet the client's behavior and feelings and modify yours as needed. You also ought to be open to what the client needs musically in the moment, and be ready to change your plans mid-session in order to meet those needs of the client.

Role reversal is another way of attempting to understand what you may need to modify. If you were the client, what could your therapist do to help build the bridge of trust? This type of role reversal exercise is a valuable means of attempting to understand your client. What kind of music therapist would you trust?

> Leave whatever is going on in your personal life outside the therapy room.

THE CLIENT CAN GUIDE YOU INTO HIS/HER OWN INTERVENTION

This is an interesting concept: Your client can teach you what to do if you are open to this concept. In order for this to occur, you have to be extremely observant, present and sensitive to what is going on in the session and with your client. Very often the music therapist gets caught up in the activity or plan of the session and can be blind to what the client really needs at the moment of intervention. Be aware of the client's reactions to music and verbalizations. I know that this is already a given in any therapeutic situation, but it really needs to be said again. If the client is not responding as you might expect, it may be because this intervention is not what the client needs at that moment. For example, if you are working with a developmentally delayed child on learning specific words, and the child seems upset, maybe what you need to be working on at that moment is expression. Until that release occurs for the client, the task that you might need to address via treatment plan may not be effectively reached because the client may not be able to focus on that task. I know what some of you are thinking, what about manipulation? Simple answer: Don't be manipulated. Manipulation is about control, and control is an issue that can be addressed and worked through.

ADJUST TREATMENT APPROACH FOR EACH CLIENT

Do not take for granted that one approach will work with another. This relates back to point number two explored in the previous section: Each client is unique even if they have the same diagnosis. Be flexible within the scope of treatment. What works with one may work with another, but because of individual differences there may be variations that are needed in your approach.

REINFORCERS ARE INDIVIDUALIZED

I learned at a young age in the University the principle that people will work for what they want. It wasn't later till I learned the principle that often what they want may not be what they need. These are two different concepts that are often misunderstood. For example, when a child wants attention, ideally we want to give a positive response to appropriate attention-getting behavior so that the child's sense of how to get attention is assimilated and learned. However, if the child wants attention and does not receive it for appropriate behavior, then the child may do something inappropriate to get his need for attention met. Attention to him/her is more important than the type of attention received. Being yelled at can be preferable to being ignored/forgotten. The message from the child is, "Hey - I want to be noticed and I will do anything to be noticed!" Therefore, you need to be aware of the reasons for the behavior. Inasmuch, ask yourself why the behavior is occurring, what is reinforcing it, and what the person working for. When you tap into what is important for the client, you have the possibility of helping the client learn how they can move forward in achieving their goals. The important thing to remember is that, what one person will work for, another person may not find as appealing.

COMMUNICATION HAPPENS
ON MANY DIFFERENT LEVELS

In therapy it is customary to listen to the words of the client to find out what is going on with them. How the client is feeling or thinking is often revealed through the expression of words, especially in verbal therapy. In listening to the words there are often additional signals that are given by the types of words used, the context in which they are used, the energy given to the words or phrase, and the associated body language that accompanies the words. A host of information can be gathered from each one of the above-mentioned signals. As you assimilate the information you will frequently see that what the person says is often not what he/she means. In many instances the words may not be congruent with what the body is doing or what is going on with the music.

The non-verbal client may still communicate with the voice even though he/she is often using sounds only meaningful to him/her. Through the careful observation of body language, facial expressions, and vocal inflections, we might be able to understand the dynamics of communication. Understanding this realm of communication is very individualized, yet when the client perceives that it is occurring with you, it is powerful in that the client may be able to progress better in the music therapy sessions. Through this process, trust and security are truly being formed.

Communication often happens on a musical level and may be accompanied by many of the behaviors previously cited. The expression of emotions through music is a difficult thing to interpret and sometimes the body language of the client can help in this process. As stated earlier, clients are unique in so many areas that when attempting to interpret the expression of emotions through music, it is often hard to summarily categorize the sounds and feelings. When viewing the client holistically in the music experience, the emotion(s) that the client is attempting to communicate might be understood.

One of the best ways to learn about the various levels of client communication is to videotape and review the tapes of the sessions from an objective viewpoint. As you watch what the client does in response to sounds, movements, questions, etc., you learn about the various levels of communication. Even better, videotape yourself as a client in a music therapy session or any creative arts therapy session and observe how you communicate to the therapist who is conducting the session. Remember, what you don't know can hurt you. By becoming a client you can be a better therapist. Learn how the client communicates and try to understand what he/she is saying.

> When viewing the client holistically in the music experience, the emotion the client is attempting to communicate might be understood.

LOOK FOR THE SMALLEST RESPONSE

A crucial part of therapy is seeing the change begin, and then working with the musical environment to make it conducive for positive growth in the client. Watching for the smallest response can be difficult because while involved in the process of the music session, so much is going on that it is quite hard to see the first signs of change. In talk therapy, you can be so singularly focused on the client that it might be easier to perceive changes, but when involved in a session such as musical improvisation, where many things are occurring, this can be much more of a challenge. Reviewing videotaped sessions is a tremendous asset for observing for the smallest signs of behavior. In this, not only can you isolate the change, but you may also be able to identify the antecedent to the behavior. By seeing this process occur, you can design and implement music therapy strategies to help further the client's progress.

PEOPLE SHOW INCREDIBLE
JOY IN ACTUAL MUSIC MAKING

Too often this is overlooked as a part of music therapy. The affect of clients who are enjoying themselves while creating, improvising, or performing music is of extreme therapeutic value. The smile and laughter that can occur during a session are often things that the client is not experiencing outside of the music therapy session. On many occasions the client who only experiences these things in music therapy will show a great desire to be part of the group and quite often this is not the same behavior other therapists might be witnessing. When you provide an environment in which joy is experienced, you are giving a rare gift to many clients where this is lacking in their lives.

IF THE FLOW IS APPROPRIATE,
GO WITH IT – DON'T BE TIED TO RIGIDITY

In school it is important to learn how to construct and follow through with session plans. These plans are maps for the developing therapist in the facilitation of a group or individual experience. At times, however, a sidetrack is warranted as the group or client may have a more pressing and immediate need of which you were initially unaware. The decision must be made as to whether to stick with the outline or to allow a different direction of the music therapy session to occur. If manipulation by the client can be ruled out, a more improvisational approach can be taken in that particular session. The more one understands the client, the easier it is to know which direction to take. In addition, the more experience one gets in the creative process of moving with what the client needs at the moment, the easier it becomes to help facilitate such an experience. Remember that a client has desires and/or problems of which you may be unaware. Respect their wishes if they give you clues indicating that they might need something else in the moment that will ultimately help them in achieving their long-term goals.

BE CAREFULLY AWARE OF YOUR EMOTIONS

As discussed earlier, being nervous as you enter your first experiences as a music therapist is normal. Getting caught up in the nervousness or anxiety is a different matter. It is important to acknowledge to yourself this nervous energy, and to be able to use it to become more aware of what is going on with the client and what he/she is offering. It is very important that you have a supervisor or support group as you enter this field to process these emotions that you go through as you are learning the art of music therapy.

Additionally, no matter what the population is or what the diagnosis might be, because you have been called to be a helper there will be emotions that will surface as you are treating your clients. You must be acutely aware of these centers of energy that become ignited as you maintain a professional relationship in the therapeutic setting. As mentioned before, you need to have an opportunity to discuss your feelings, reactions, and concerns on a regular basis.

BEING "TRIGGERED" BY THE CLIENT

This item comes on the heels of the one discussed previously, as it is again an emotional issue. To be "triggered" means that on an unconscious, almost automatic level, something occurs that puts you emotionally into a bad place that you have been in before. The event that sets this all into motion may be only obliquely related to the original event, but there is something serving as a reminder to put you emotionally into a place that is not beneficial for your client.

So what happens if you are triggered? The moment you realize that your focus on the client has been diverted and your own issue(s) have somehow surfaced, you must get yourself out of that frame of mind. Refocus on your client, become aware of how he/she needs you at this moment. Then, as mentioned before, get supervision, support or counseling so you have an outlet to explore the issue. These issues will not just go away. They are a part of you, and you need to learn how to integrate them into who you are so that you can always be present for your client.

Put in place a support system where you
can process your
feelings and experiences.

CERTAIN CLIENTS CAN AND WILL MANIPULATE YOU

No one likes to be manipulated. Sometimes you might be dealing with the client who is a master at manipulation. The client can be at any cognitive level and still be a manipulator. Manipulation might be an unconscious pattern for the client resulting in some sort of gain, or it might be conscious in that the client wishes to steer the session in a different direction. Initially you may not know that you are being manipulated so when you feel that things have just gone wrong, you should always question whether the client has manipulated you or not. If you feel that you have been manipulated, begin to notice the patterns in which this occurs. Reflect on the behavior of the client and the conditions in which in the event occurs. Be creative in figuring out a strategy to stop the manipulation before it has a chance to develop. If you are working with a cognitive, verbal client, you can sometimes just stop and describe to the client what is happening and question him/her as to what is behind the behavior.

With clients who are less cognitive and possibly nonverbal, try to find an intervention that will break the behavior pattern. Remember that the client will be getting some kind of "stroke" out of the manipulation, so your job is to structure for a response that breaks the manipulative behavior and allows them to experience a "stroke" that is related to a more productive outcome.

RESPECT THE PHYSICAL SPACE OF YOUR CLIENT

Sometimes in our eagerness to be close and/or physically reinforcing we are not aware that the client's personal space is being violated by our actions and our behavior may be perceived in quite an opposite way from which it was intended. Some clients are touch-sensitive and in doing your homework on the client you will discover whether this is true. Check with other therapists or refer to documentation for further assistance with this. The client may have been abused in some manner and your presence may be perceived as threatening. I find that asking permission with verbal, cognitive clients, is a good first step prior to touching them. In some cases you may just inform the client that you will be close to him/her or that you are about to touch them. When helping a client play an instrument, this approach is often good as it prepares the client for this intervention.

BE AWARE OF FLYING DRUMSTICKS

Clients can and will throw instruments as well as objects that play instruments. There is a chapter later that addresses many types of disruptive behaviors and intervention strategies for them. I mention this now only to make the point that this is something we can learn from our clients: They have the potential to be destructive and possibly hurt us in the process. Utmost care should be taken in the discovery of possible dangerous behaviors. At times it may be necessary to have help in the room, as not having it could put your safety as well as that of the client, at risk.

ADAPT THE PACE OF YOUR
SESSION TO YOUR CLIENT(S)

Pacing with groups and individual clients is critical. Pacing is the rhythmic flow of the session, how things are presented and the timing of them. Within each session a pace will be developed. That pace can be dictated by you, the client, or by a cooperative effort. Being aware of this can be helpful in that if you are dictating the pace and the client can't keep up, you need to adjust the flow. If the client is dictating it may be a manipulation or an indication that you might not be in touch with his/her needs in the moment. When working together, there is a sense that you are moving with them in a "give and take" mode. The session has a flow that is conducive to the client's progress.

KNOW YOUR CLIENT'S POTENTIAL

Through the assessment process you learn about the things that the client can and cannot do. Using the strengths of the client to help in those areas that are not as strong is a common therapeutic technique. Knowing how to spark the success process within each client is a tool that will enable the relationship to further the goals of the client. At times when there is a sense of frustration in the client you can use this idea to build confidence, increase self-esteem, and re-establish direction.

KNOW WHO YOUR STAFF IS AND
HOW THEY REACT TO YOUR SESSIONS

While this is not something that we learn from our clients, it is something that we can learn while working with our clients. There are many professional staff members that are helpful, supportive and appropriate during the sessions. On the other hand you may run into staff members that use this time to fulfill, on some level, their own needs. This can happen with almost any clientele. When it does happen, it can often be distracting for the clients as well as for you. A tactful handling of the situation is necessary and can often be done without alienating the staff member.

> *Setting:* The staff member joined in on an improvisation and controlled the rhythm of the group. After the session you address what happened.
> *Music Therapist:* It seemed that you really enjoyed that playing.
> *Staff:* Yeah… it was really <u>fun</u>.
> *Music Therapist:* I'm happy you had <u>fun</u> with it. I was noticing that John (client) was getting emotional, did you see that?
> *Staff:* Not really.
> *Music Therapist:* Maybe next time you can sit out and help me by really watching the expression of the clients as they play. I would really like your feedback on them.

An inappropriate exchange might go like this:

> *Music Therapist:* You were really banging that drum hard!
> *Staff:* Yea… it was really fun.
> *Music Therapist:* Well, it might be for you, but the clients certainly didn't enjoy it. Don't you know that this is therapy for them and not for you!

In the first example, the staff member was acknowledged and then asked to be an integral part of the session in another way. Giving a willing staff member a purpose and then expressing gratitude for their work will go a long way in helping the sessions as well as the work environment.

SOMETHING SPECIAL IS HAPPENING

We often see clients from a perspective that other professionals cannot access, for being involved in the music allows the client to be creative in an environment that is not duplicated by any other therapy.

> Unique events occur in music therapy
> sessions that are not seen
> in other types of therapy.

To see children smile when that response is basically lacking in their lives, to hear adults process music and find connections and solutions to their issues through the music that may not be found in strict verbal therapy, and to hear an aged person reminisce about all that is good are just a few of the wonderful things that can occur in music therapy. These are often the real rewards of being a music therapist. Through these events our clients teach us and remind us that something special is happening in these music therapy sessions. It is important as you gain experience, and at times feel "burnt out," to keep the focus on the client and remember how special this all is.

SUMMARY

The client can be your best teacher regarding how to properly do music therapy. The client is the primary receiver of the benefit of the therapy session, but if you have developed your reflective skills and have the opportunity to video-tape your sessions, you can learn a great deal about what works and doesn't, about your style development, and about how to best serve the client.

Through this chapter the headings that were given were based on the real life experiences of music therapy students reflecting on their fieldwork. These do not include all of the things that clients can teach us but they do encompass many areas related to this subject. Being open to this concept so that you can learn more, develop more, and become a more effective music therapist will further your significance with the clients that you serve.

Chapter 4

TALKING AS AN INTERVENTION

There are many things that can happen when the music stops, and one of these is a verbal intervention. There are a variety of verbal techniques that can be employed at this moment in a music therapy session, and the type of technique utilized is dependent upon two main factors. The first of these factors is the developmental level of the client with whom you are working. The second is the goal of the session.

The developmental level of the client refers to his/her diagnosis as well as intellectual and behavioral functioning level. If a client is diagnosed with mental retardation or autism and has limited or no verbal skills, the types of verbal responses you will employ after the music stops are quite different from those you would use with an adolescent with a conduct disorder or an adult diagnosed with depression. With a client that has limited verbal skills your verbal response may be minimal and directed toward the concrete task at hand. With the adolescent and/or adult, the above approach may also be used but the subsequent interaction and dialogue may be quite different. There may be exploration of feelings or cognitive questions employed to gather more information.

The goal of the session also needs consideration. Using the above examples of different functioning levels of the clients, the corresponding goals might also be different. The goal of the first (an autistic or developmentally delayed child) might be maintaining eye contact for five seconds. The goal of the second (an adolescent with conduct disorder or a depressed adult) could possibly be to cooperate with members in the group and/or share a feeling. Although your role is similar for both in that you are the music therapist, the method of music therapy changes. With the first client you may be more of an objective observer for the desired response in relation to the music intervention. This does not mean that you are detached from care for the client from a humanistic perspective, but rather the role you have is to facilitate a response that is needed to help the client develop further toward his/her goals. Your response to the client may be verbal or kinesthetic, and may provide immediate feedback to the client as to how he/she is doing in relationship to the desired outcome. The adolescent or depressed adult may require verbal interaction that is quite different from the previous client. Since the second client is more cognitive, a different verbal interaction may be used. Here your role as therapist might be to help the client see cause and effect relationships regarding his/her behavior, enable verbalization about the feelings of the session, and enable cognitive insight regarding other aspects of behavior and/or feelings.

Whether one is processing previously recorded music, an improvisation, or using music to direct/facilitate a task at hand, there will come a time when verbal skills are required. The higher functioning the population, the more skilled you will need to be in verbal techniques.

When working with cognitive clients the interaction can become more involved on a verbal level. This chapter introduces and illustrates various techniques with this as a premise. With that premise being set, know that this chapter is **not** a substitute for advanced training in verbal psychotherapy.

PHILOSOPHICAL ORIENTATION

For the most part, a basic philosophical orientation that you have internalized as part of your therapeutic style is brought into the music therapy session and guides you on how to verbally proceed within that contextual (philosophical) framework. The content of this chapter, however, does not classify to what counseling theory these verbalizations will ultimately fall under and is not addressed. The techniques that are given below are intended to help you find a comfortable style of communicating with the client on a verbal level and may ultimately fit into several different theoretical approaches. You may notice, however, that as you use these, some will not fit into your own sense or content of "style" that you are developing. Throughout this chapter, examples and interventions are offered in order to give you a base level of competence from which to build. These are merely suggestions to get you started and are by no means the end result of who you should become as a "Music Therapist." The development of your skill level begins with the basic equipment of who you are, where you have been in your life, and what you ultimately bring to the session.

At first you may want to practice these and variations of them in a lab setting. After familiarity is developed it is recommended not to use these techniques verbatim. Use the concepts, and variations of them, to become part of you and your style.

THE QUESTION

When the music stops, the client(s) are often waiting for what is to happen next and are looking for your lead. You have just facilitated some type of music therapy intervention and now the music part is temporarily suspended. What do you do if the client does not initiate a verbal response? Do you feel an awkward silence? It might be time to ask a question.

There are two types of questions, the "close-ended" question and the "open-ended" question. Here are a couple of examples of the "close-ended question":

> *Music Therapist:* "Do you want to play the drum now?"
> *Client:* "No."
> *Music Therapist:* "Can you tell me more about that?"
> *Client:* "No."

The choice that is left for the client in a "close-ended" question is a "yes" or "no" answer, meaning they can avoid offering any further information as they have already answered the question. The focus (perhaps pressure) is then placed back on you to try to get the client to open up and share. This situation can be avoided through asking the open-ended question, and then waiting patiently for the response.

The open-ended question allows the client to offer information and is often the starting point in the verbal process. In many talk therapies the first thing that the therapist will ask after you sit down in front of her/him is, "So, what's going on with you?" This gives the opportunity and invitation to begin speaking without giving a "yes" or "no" answer. In music therapy, your initial open-ended question should be based on the music experience that has just occurred. It is often formed from an observation that you had of the client:

"I noticed that.......... What was happening then for you?"
"As you played the drum, you went into a strong rhythm. I'm curious as to why you did that?"
"As you listened, you closed your eyes. What were you (imagining) (thinking about)?"

It might be based on an interaction with the client. For example:

"You were playing this melody as I played the chords on the piano. What was going on for you in those moments?"
"What was it like to have me play the drum so intensely with you?"
"I am curious about what it was like for you to have me playing this pattern (bass ostinato) in the background of your improvisation."

Open-ended questions often begin with here, what, who, when, or why. When you can formulate these in your mind prior to speaking, you have a greater chance of engaging the client in dialogue.

> Starting with what has happened
> for the client in the music,
> formulate an open-ended question.

The basic idea for this opening question is to utilize what happened during the session as a basis for discussion. Notice also that I did not put the "How are you feeling right now" question into the above mix. While at times it might be a valid question, I have found that many therapists often overuse it and in the music therapy experience we can learn about the client's emotional state by focusing on his/her responses to and interactions with the music. Additionally, clients who are in treatment will often reject this question because it is asked of them so frequently during the day that its impact is often diminished.

A good way to develop this skill is to observe various sessions and then try to formulate phrases drawn from the music experience that you can use. Even if you are observing a non-verbal client, you can notice aspects of the interaction and then write down an appropriate open-ended question that you would present to the client if he/she were verbal.

A common pitfall in the scope of asking a question, is asking too many questions in rapid succession:

> *Music Therapist*: "What were you thinking about? Did something come to mind? Were you able to focus on the sound?"

This can obviously be confusing for a client and it is something that experience and thoughtfulness can remedy. Offer only one question at a time. After the presentation of the question patience may be required. Often in the moments of silence, while the client is processing the question, you may feel a need to clarify what was asked. Instead, be quiet and patient and let the process unfold. If a long period of time elapses it may then be appropriate to see if clarification is warranted. If you need to clarify then do so using a simple phrase, and continue to be patient. The silence is a time when both you and the client can process what is going on. For the client, he/she has just been involved in a music experience and the shift back to the verbal experience might need a little time. He/she may be going through a process of clarifying thoughts and feelings that have occurred during the musical experience.

> Offer only one question at a time.
> Be patient, your client needs
> time to process the question.

It is quite possible that a client will be resistant even with a gentle open-ended question.

> *Music Therapist:* "As you listened, you closed your eyes. What were you (imagining) (thinking about)?"
> *Client:* "Nothing."

When this type of response occurs there are several things to consider:

- The client was actually off-task while engaged in the musical activity and does not want to admit it.
- The client is not comfortable sharing this information with you.
- The client is resistant to the thought of sharing information in this setting.
- The events are too painful to verbalize at this time.

Being able to handle this response is a skill that many of the following techniques will help address. For example, a simple restatement of the word "nothing" is a technique when it is said within the musical framework in which it is presented. If the client says, "nothing," slowly with an upward inflection, you may want to mirror this sound, do the opposite, or present it back as a simple question: "Nothing?" Notice the music of his/her body language as they say the word, as that is something else that can be brought to their attention.

Music Therapist: I noticed that when you said the word "nothing" you crossed your legs and seemed to withdraw. Maybe there is something to that?

Here are some examples of what not to say:

- Don't say, "Certainly you saw something."
- Don't say, "I don't believe that."
- Don't say, "Everyone sees something to this – so you must have also."

These replies discount the response of the client. Remember that all responses are valid responses and you need to use the response as information that is given to you by the client. As it is information, it is your responsibility to accept this response and work with it as much as you can. I say, "as much as you can," because the client may shut down on you during the session and his/her "response" may be a total lack of response. It might mean that you need to take a different musical direction, sit in silence for a time, or perhaps even consider ending the session early. It is again important to point out that this is not a time to take the response of the client personally. Keep the focus on the client and the intervention, not on yourself.

VERBAL TECHNIQUES

The techniques that are presented below are meant as starting points as you develop your style. They are given to help guide you in the direction you might take when various types of responses are given. They can, however, be misused. If you tend to use the same one over and over again with the client, he/she will anticipate your response instead of being in the process. Learn them, practice them, and be cognizant of your utilization of them. These are ways to help the client process the session and the musical material in order to facilitate personal growth.

Verbal Reflection of Feelings/Music

This is the recognition of the client's feelings and subsequent mirroring of those feelings.

> *Situation:* The client finishes an improvisation of a minor melody in a relatively slow rhythm on the piano.
> *Music Therapist:* That was quite a moving melody. I'm curious as to what was going on for you as you played it. (*Notice that the therapist does not label the improvisation with a feeling or ask for a current feeling*).
> *Client:* I was thinking about when I was a little girl and I was all alone. (*The rhythm of the sentence was slow and the melody minimal in range - similar to the improvisation. There is seemingly congruence between the emotion felt and the music improvised.*)

There are many choices now – one might be to mirror the melody on the piano and ask the client to reflect on the image, again requesting more detail. Another technique is choosing one or two words and reflecting them back to the client.

> *Music Therapist:* So you were **alone** when you were a **little girl**? (*Note the utilization of the same language of the client.*)

This technique is not a "Parrot" type of strategy where you simply repeat what was just said. Instead you are actually in the moment with the client (Presence – Empathy) and reflecting the emotion.

If there is incongruence between the music and the emotion, be similar in your response and note that there might be some confusion in the client regarding an issue. A lack of congruence on a consistent basis may point to more serious cognitive/emotional issues that can be difficult to resolve. For example, in a group that was listening and creating imagery to the *Finale* of the *Firebird Suite* by Igor Stravinsky, almost all of the group members were imagining majestic mountains, sunrises, etc. One young man described his images as being of soldiers marching into a town to slaughter the village. This, while being valid for the client, was not the norm for this activity or group. So you might ask, "How was this handled?" I first validated the images by saying, "Those are interesting scenes John, (using his name to try to get more grounded in the moment), maybe we can talk about them more later." I then immediately documented this session and checked with him a little later, at which time he declined to go further into the discussion (this was also documented in the chart).

This particular technique of reflection helps in the development of trust and rapport. The client begins to feel comfortable in the session and often feels like someone is beginning to understand him/her.

Restatement of Content

The client's words are summarized through interpreting the cognitive content of what was said. While the first technique of reflection focuses on feelings, this strategy focuses on the reflection of cognitive ideas. The thoughts of the client are often closely related to the feelings of the client. For example, when you ask a client what they think of a piece of music, he/she will often tell you how they are actually *feeling* about the music. It can be subtle, but when you can "hear between the lines" the thoughts often reflect a feeling-based response.

Restatement of content also enables either a beginning, or a continuation of rapport. The client will realize at some level that there is a connection happening and that he/she is understood. Furthermore, with the musical involvement, the client may be feeling connections on many different levels.

> When you ask clients what they thought about the music, they are actually giving you what they felt about the music.

Situation: The client just listened to an instrumental selection from *West Side Story* by Leonard Bernstein and was instructed to think of any images that came to mind.
Music Therapist: What did you think of that? (*Notice that the question is not asking for a feeling state.*)
Client: I thought of being on a busy street in New York City … everything was moving fast like in a big city.
Music Therapist: So it was **busy** and energetic? (*Energetic is the restatement of moving fast – without repeating the same words.*)
Client: Yeah. It was really fast with cars all over the place.

So in this example the restatement is not of a feeling but of a thought. When a client says, "all over the place," there is an indication that the thought might be more chaotic. The music therapist may then want to pursue that avenue (chaos) as a topic.

Noticing the Incongruence

Noticing the discrepancies between client's actions, words, feelings and music can lead you to a point where you might confront the client regarding these behaviors. Confrontation, however, is not encouraged in the early part of therapy. You need to initially establish a rapport and relationship and take note of general behavioral patterns that are incongruent. When you first bring up the incongruence, it should be done in a gentle manner and can often be presented in the form of a question.

> *Situation*: The client has just finished a drumming improvisation that is slow and laborious. When asked to give a title to what was just improvised, he/she calls it "High Energy."
> *Music Therapist:* If you gave this improvisation a title, what would it be?
> *Client:* High Energy. (*Given in a monotone and lethargic voice.*)
> *Music Therapist:* High Energy?
> *Client:* Yeah.
> *Music Therapist:* I noticed that your playing wasn't very loud or fast. I'm wondering if this is what "high energy" sounds like for you?

This response gives the client several bits of information. First, the music therapist restates the title as a question, which prompts another verbal response. The music therapist then objectifies the sound that was heard, but done in such a way that the client can still feel as if he/she was heard and understood. The music therapist then presents an open-ended question that includes in it the title the client initially gave. The client's incongruence is addressed in a very non-threatening manner wherein there is still acceptance and validation of the original response.

Following are several examples of incongruence:

- Facial expression and words (laughing while telling a sad part of a story)
- Gross body language and words (crossing legs tightly while saying that he/she is open to the process)
- Fine motor skills and words (picking at the fingers nervously while saying nothing is wrong)
- Description of musical events and any of the above (as given in the example above)

Use Your Own Words Sparingly

In general, you should be brief in your verbal interactions by talking less than the client except when summarizing. By talking too much you may bring in your own projections, thus leading the client away from what he/she might be leading you to. I often like to summarize the session leading up to a final question for the clients to comment on or answer.

Notice the poor interaction in the following example:

> *Situation:* The client has just finished playing an improvisation with you on a pentatonic xylophone.
> *Music Therapist*: Nice improvisation! It was really neat how the rhythm you played was so steady and how you put so much feeling into playing that one note over and over again. Can you give it a title?
> *Client:* Tired.
> *Music Therapist:* Yeah, tired, I know exactly what you mean, I am tired too. You played it like you were really tired, probably tired of your relationship. I can understand that because of all the things that you have been going through. Your loss of work and your girlfriend, you have been through so much. Tired…. I know exactly what you mean.

In this example there is too much of everything by the music therapist. The client may be really tired of just listening to the music therapist, but never has a chance to verbalize this. I think that example speaks for itself: Be brief and avoid the above diatribe.

It is OK to be Silent

When you don't know what to say, say nothing. If you do know what to say, ask yourself if this is the appropriate time to say it. The "rest" sign in music indicates silence. This aspect of music creates and provides for space, breath, rest, anticipation, release, and tension. In the moments after the music stops, or during the discussion, silence can create all of these musical elements. Silence has purpose in music as it does in the music therapy session. In the "space" of the silence, you and the client can assimilate what is happening in the moment. In the "breath" of the silence you can check your client's breathing patterns as well as your own. You may need to focus on your own breath for a moment to be increasingly present for the client. In the "rest" of the silence you and your client may need this time to just sit back and – rest. The silence can create "anticipation" – the feeling that something important is about to happen, be realized, or be verbalized. In the "release" in the silence there is often an emotional release through the acknowledgement of the emotion. And in the "tension" of the silence, there is a seeking of further expression leading ultimately to a resolution.

> Silence/quiet time is required in all
> aspects of life and music.

Silence is an essential aspect of music as well as of the music therapy session. It is ultimately the responsibility of the client to fill in the silence of the discussion time. Be aware of the meaning of the silence. If it goes too long, and the session is stagnating, ask an open-ended question.

> *Situation:* After a brief discussion of some poetry the client (Theresa) wrote to an instrumental selection, there is a long period of silence. The client has stopped looking at the words on the paper and is gazing off to their side. Nothing has been said for over a minute.
> *Music Therapist:* Theresa ...... what's going on for you right now?

The question is addressing the client's present situation. It is appropriate in that it seems that the client has become stuck in a moment and the silence is enabling him/her to stay in that moment.

There are times in sessions when you do not really know what to say. It is best at these times to say nothing at all. Survey the meaning of the silence, and get a feel for its purpose. Be with the client in the silence and see where it leads. The client may ultimately break the silence, or you may just need time to develop a question as in the above example.

The Modulation Through Process

A therapeutic process involves the discussion of feelings, thoughts and/or behaviors leading to insight and change. In music, modulation refers to a change in keys, or tonal centers. This change can be abrupt (like a light bulb going on), or more gradual and unraveling, such as a sequence of a motif that takes you into a new tonal area. Similarly, the treatment of a fragmented thought or feeling can be in essence "sequenced" (as in music) through to help the client arrive at a new place (tonal center).

Processing means actively talking about what is going on. It often begins with the discussion of the music and leads to the investigation of feelings, thoughts and behaviors. Comments usually focus on the "here and now" experience – what the client is feeling and experiencing at that moment. It can be initiated by the music therapist as a reaction to what he/she observes from the client.

> *Situation:* The client has just listened to the recording of an improvisation that he/she had done in the previous session. The client played the feelings of "frustration" on a large drum. It was recorded and the client was not able to process the improvisation at that time.
>
> *Music Therapist:* That was last week's improvisation. What were you thinking as you listened to it? *(Once again notice that the question is asking for a cognitive assessment, not emotional, thus keeping away from the "How did it make you feel?" type of question. The client in response focuses on the emotional aspect.)*
>
> *Client:* It sounded angry. *(2 pieces of information are given – one is that the client refers to the improvisation as "it" and does not take the ownership of the feeling yet. Second – it is now "angry" when he/she originally wanted "frustration.")*
>
> *Music Therapist:* Angry?
>
> *Client:* Angry… like really it was really pissed off.
>
> *Music Therapist:* What about it sounded angry?

At this point you can see the direction it is taking. There would then be a discussion of the sounds of frustration and anger, leading to an exploration of the feelings and the associations and why they are being felt at this moment in time. The next step would involve telling the client that you notice the improvisation is an "it," while it was an "I" that created it. From here the modulation of feelings and thoughts is beginning to occur through the process of discussion. Notice that in the process of discussion there are techniques that were used to explore information which were presented earlier in this chapter. Process leads to change as modulation leads to new keys. The ways in which these are both accomplished are inherently similar.

Opposition Can Be Conscious or Unconscious

The resistance of a client can block the process of the music therapy session. This can be done in many different ways and can be motivated consciously and/or unconsciously. When you notice that this is happening with a client, it sometimes signals that you are properly maintaining focus where it needs to be. It is not usually the case that the client is being deliberately resistive to upset or confuse you. Instead, the behavior needs to be viewed as information that the client is giving you about his/her current state. With this in mind, some of the ways a client may show resistance in the music therapy session are: forgetting, changing the subject (going off task), or simply refusing to get involved in a music therapy experience.

> Clients are always giving you
> information. Even if it seems
> resistive and counter productive,
> it is still information.

Situation: The client forgets something that was supposed to be done.
Music Therapist: Last week we spoke about bringing that CD that reminded you of some really happy moments in your life. I am looking forward to hearing that.
Client: Oh yeah. I'm sorry, I forgot that.

There are several different ways to handle this situation.

- Ask the client to do the assignment again and develop a strategy to remember.
- Point out that in forgetting it often means that the subject matter is being avoided at some level, and discuss as to why this was avoided.
- Let it go for now. Take note and if it happens again (which it probably will as this is a way for the client not to engage), begin to process this aspect of resistance.

Situation: Client is beginning to process a response to a selection of music and changes the topic
Client: I really like that piece. It reminded me of being up in the mountains – taking it easy. (*Long pause.*) I was thinking about getting a new car – what do think?

Here is an abrupt change and it can be addressed by immediately bringing the change to the client's attention. Then move to the feeling that was about to be processed.

Music Therapist: You just changed topics in mid-thought; let's get back to how the music took you into your thoughts of the mountains.

In this you have brought to the client's attention what just happened and can now process that occurrence.

Music Therapist: So – you went from being up in the mountains to the thought of buying a new car.

Some possible questions might be:

- How did you make this switch?
- Why did you make this switch?
- What is it about the thought of being in the mountains that led you to the thought of a new car?

Situation: The client simply does not want to be in music therapy at this time (this is assuming that the client has been in music therapy before).

This can occur for a myriad of reasons:

- He/she may be feeling afraid of having a strong emotional reaction.
- He/she may have had a tough day already and needs to rest.
- He/she may be angry at someone or something and are dwelling in that emotion or are stuck in this feeling (which in itself is another type of resistance – choosing to be stuck in an emotional state).
- By thinking less of music therapy – "This stuff is stupid", he/she is really being self-protective and not willing to take chances.
- Music therapy just might not be the best therapeutic approach at this time (which may also fit in with the previous area of not thinking highly of the modality).

Your strategy at this time needs to be based on which of the above you think is occurring for the client. Each one can be worked with in some fashion. Even the last two might mean that you simply converse with the client for a short period of time. Perhaps through the conversation the client will open up and give more information at which time you can introduce the idea of music again. Even in these cases you can employ the next section of technique – when in doubt, focus on the feeling.

When in Doubt, Focus on the Feeling

Focusing on the feelings or the musical sounds of feelings can often help the client find his/her way through the emotion. The only way that a client can truly come out of an emotion is to move through it. Feelings can be talked about, written about, illustrated, danced or moved through, dramatized, and set to music. Earlier I said that when you don't know what to say it is often best to be silent. The session might be at a point, however, where being silent is not the best strategy. To focus on the emotions that the client might be going through "in the moment" can often help the client get through an event. It might be that this is where the client often progresses to in a talk therapy situation and then cannot move forward simply by talking. If the moment is sparked by musical stimulation, then the client might be more acutely aware of the feeling being aroused within him/her and verbalization might be easier.

In concentrating on the feeling, there are the "Big Four" feelings under which all others can be listed. They are: Anger, Sadness, Fear, and Joy. The verbal language of feelings is an important language to understand as it often describes the reaction to the musical event. David Martin in *Counseling and Therapy Skills* (1989) lists the shadings of verbal language that fall under the "Big Four."

UNHAPPY WORDS: dejected, low, sad, depressed, down, lost, blue, melancholy, brood, dreary, flat, joyless, downhearted, somber, gloomy, dreadful, dismal, empty, grim, desolate, hopeless, mourning, desperate, blah, glum, disappointed, aching, anguish, grieving, rotten, barren, awful, teary, terrible.

AFFECTION WORDS: love, friendly, caring, like, fond of, respect, admire, trust, close, adore, devoted, regard, tenderness, attachment, yearning, longing, infatuated, fellowship, attraction, favor, prize, hold dear, fall for, passionate, revere, cherish, idolize.

GUILT WORDS: blame, regret, shame, embarrassed, at fault, reprehensible, wrong, remorseful, crummy, rotten, humiliated, unforgivable, mortified, ashamed, disgraceful.

ANGER WORDS: resentment, irritation, rage, fury, annoyance, provoked, infuriated, inflamed, displeasure, animosity, wrath, indignation, exasperation, pique, huff, miff, sore, bitter, temper, hate, fume, dander, torment, tiff, passion, sullen, morose, bristle, bridle, sulk, pout, frown, chafe, seethe, boil, rage, offend, rile, aggravate, rankle, worked up, cross, burning, pissed off, outraged, ticked off, hateful, vengeful, mad.

FEAR WORDS: timid, diffident, anxious, worried, apprehensive, misgiving, doubt, qualm, hesitant, fright, terror, horror, dismay, panic, consternation, scared, nervous, restless, trepidation, quivering, shaking, trembling, intimidated, cold sweat, dread, despondent, creeps, shivers, jitters, cower, afraid, tremulous, vulnerable, butterflies, jumpy, worried, uneasy, unsure.

CONFUSED WORDS: bewildered, puzzled, flustered, overwhelmed, mixed up, muddled, perplexed, tumult, chaos, jumbled, uncertain, undecided, ambivalent, drifting, baffled, trapped, in a quandary, tangled, scrambled, unraveled, disjointed, swamped, drowning, frustrated.

HAPPY WORDS: contented, joyous, ecstatic, glad, cheerful, glee, optimistic, hopeful, alive, lively, merry, exhilarate, jovial, satisfied, comfortable, animated, inspired, elated, encouraged, heartened, refreshed, genial, light, buoyant, bright, saucy, jolly, playful, exultant, pleased, gratified, zest, bliss, thrilled, tickled, sensational, terrific, euphoric, enthusiastic, glowing, neat, good, fine.

HURT WORDS: neglected, put down, rejected, demeaned, scorned, used, criticized, belittled, shot down, cast off, discarded, let down, disappointed, devastated, humiliated, betrayed, harmed, embarrassed, dumped on, ripped off, disillusioned, disparaged, maligned, laughed at, exploited.

STRENGTH WORDS: responsible, competent, adequate, powerful, certain, sure, efficient, important, competent, effective, superior, cope, potent, able, lucid, adaptable, forceful, effectual, incisive, influential, growing, moving forward, alive.

Being aware of how words are used to describe emotional states is an asset as it gives you a common ground in talking with the client. By using similar "feeling" words you can help the client describe the emotion as well as empathize with the client in the feeling. Musically depicting the various words that are used can help channel the emotion into a non-verbal expression, which is often where emotions are best expressed. The energy of the emotion is often not adequately dispensed through words, but words are needed to help codify the emotional issues so that a common language can be utilized and understood.

> *Situation:* The client is attempting to describe what is happening emotionally after hearing a song.
> *Client:* I'm not sure what I am feeling (*confusion indicated*).
> *Music Therapist:* Sometimes things seem mixed up (*confusion words used and then a solution offered*). Try finding one or two words from the song to help you.
> *Client:* I like it when she says "be with me." (*silence*)
> *Music Therapist*: (*remains silent – patience*)
> *Client*: It makes me feel warm … accepted.
> *Music Therapist*: Warm and accepted. (*Mirror the sound and phrase it in a similar voice*). I hear tenderness as you say that.
> *Client*: Yea. It's a nice feeling.

From here there can be more dialogue leading to a musical improvisation about how these emotions might sound. A piece could then possibly be composed and recorded for further use. The words used to describe the feelings are significant in this process. Eventually, bringing the music back into the session becomes important for further expression and possibly closure.

> Often the client can best express
> an emotion through music.

I know that I have avoided the following phrase often in this book as well as in my practice: "How did that make you feel?" One of the reasons I avoid this is that if you believe that something "*makes* you feel" a certain way, you can avoid taking responsibility for the feeling. In reality, we choose feelings in order to experience what we unconsciously need to gain in a given situation. Not accepting responsibility for a feeling or behavior is often what a client uses to hamper his/her own progress in life. By saying, "How does this music make you feel?", we are enabling the client's avoidance of responsibility.

Questions or statements that can replace the one above and hopefully get to the heart of the emotion are listed below. Remember to focus on the current situation.

- I noticed something about you as you listened (played). I am curious as to what feelings you are having right now.
- I know that there are many emotions that go on while listening to (or playing) music. I was wondering what emotion(s) you were going through.
- It seems that you are experiencing something. What is going on for you right now?
- Please put into words what just happened with you.
- Tell me what you are feeling right now.

> We choose feelings in order to experience what we unconsciously need to gain in a given situation.

Notice When a Metaphor is Being Used

A metaphor is a figure of speech in which a word or phrase that ordinarily designates one thing is used to designate another, thus making an implicit comparison. When a client uses a metaphor as part of his/her process, it is good to investigate it as well as any musical reflections or interpretations.

Client: I feel like a big weight has been lifted off my shoulders.
Music Therapist: It seems you are relieved?
Client: Yeah – I actually feel lighter!
Music Therapist: That's great! Since we have done work with so many heavy sounds, perhaps we can explore some new sounds or music to help describe this feeling.

Another example:

Client: I feel like I'm missing a piece of the <u>puzzle</u>.
Music Therapist: So – when a piece of a <u>puzzle</u> is missing, it is usually hard to finish.
Client: It is hard to finish …
Music Therapist: Sometimes it can be frustrating, at other times, confusing … I'm curious as to whether any of these words <u>fit</u> (*like in a puzzle*) what is going on for you right now?

Here the feeling behind the statement is being explored. Musically, this can be illustrated by playing an instrument like a xylophone, without a mallet. Once the right solution is found or connections made, things usually become easier to process– such as in playing the instrument.

> When metaphors are used by the client,
> explore them verbally and musically.

What the Body is Really Saying

The nonverbal communications of the client are difficult to censor. It is often through the body that messages of a feeling state are being presented.

Areas to be aware of are:

- Nodding or the shaking of the head while talking
- Crossed arms and/or legs and how much tension is in them

- Facial expressions such as smiles and frowns
- Voice tone, rhythm and melody
- Psychokinetic tension where there is a rapid movement of a body part (as in foot shaking repeatedly)
- Eye contact
- Breathing patterns
- Gross body (closing up the body as in a fetal position or the opposite of this) and fine body (playing with a ring on a finger while talking about commitment) movement that seems to be meaningful
- Laughter and tears

When you notice that body language is in agreement with verbal processing or a musical improvisation, it affirms that which the client is telling you. If there is incongruence, then you need to decide how to approach the situation. A phrase to help you in this situation begins with "I notice that," after which you describe the incongruence.

The first example shows incongruence between verbal and body language.

> *Situation:* While client was free-associating to an instrumental piece of music, he/she folded his/her arms and legs while talking about being a happy 12–year-old.

> *Music Therapist:* I noticed that as you began speaking of when you were 12, you folded up your arms and legs quite tightly. I am curious as to what was really going on for you at that age.

Body language can also come into play when a client is engaged in playing an instrument in a musical activity. The next example relates to this instance.

> *Situation:* The client is improvising various emotions that are being processed through the session. The client decides to play a large drum to explore the word "energy." The client plays with very strong hits on the drum in a straight rhythm. The mallets are held

very tightly and the face of the client begins to turn a bit red and intense.

Client: That was <u>energy</u> for me.

Music Therapist: It certainly had a lot of <u>energy</u> in it. I noticed as you were playing, that your face became red and very intense.

Client: Really? I do feel a little <u>warm</u>.

Music Therapist: Expending energy can get us <u>warm,</u> but I am wondering if it is more than that. It was very intense and I noticed that you held the mallets with a very strong grip. I wonder what was really going on.

In this example, the discovery of what is really going on for the client is being shaped through the conversation by noticing the body language and how it relates to what the client said. Here is an example of what <u>not</u> to say in this same situation:

Client: That was <u>energy</u> for me.

Music Therapist: No it wasn't – it was anger.

The therapist jumps in and discounts the response of the client and comes to a conclusion that the client is not prepared to hear. This interaction leads us into the next topic.

Avoid Trying to Solve the Client's Problem

Sometimes you feel that it is your responsibility to make the client's problems go away. You may often want to give advice and suggest strategies to help resolve the problems of the client. It is the ultimate responsibility of the client to resolve his or her own issues. We create a unique musical environment for this to occur. Our job is to help guide the client through the process of self-discovery. It is not our job to attempt to tell the client what he/she is "really" feeling or to give advice on how to solve the problem.

How to Bring Closure to a Session

I suggest ending a session by summarizing what has been accomplished and possibly where to go from the experience. As the session comes to an end it is often good to let the client know that the time is almost finished. In this way, abrupt endings are avoided as the client is aware that the time is almost over. Earlier in the chapter I alluded to this, as it is the time in the session when I speak the most. It is my desire to help the client summarize what took place from both an objective and subjective point of view. When helping the client come to the end of the experience I usually help him/her examine one or more of the following:

- What will be taken or remembered from the session.
- What has been accomplished.
- What has been learned.
- What was different for him/her.
- Is there a change in the emotional state?
- Is there a change in the cognitive state?
- Is there a change in the physical state?
- What can be applied in reality for them – the future.

SUMMARY

This chapter introduces verbal techniques that you can utilize to facilitate the non-music process of the music therapy session. While the music experience is the primary therapeutic technique (thus the term "Music Therapy"), there are many opportunities for verbal interaction and processing, especially when the music stops.

> This chapter is not intended as a
> substitute for advanced training
> in verbal psychotherapy.

The primary population addressed in this chapter is one that is fairly cognitive and verbal. This does not mean that this chapter is exclusive to this population, as many of these techniques will be useful with other clientele. It is never-the-less offered as a guideline for interaction with the more verbal and cognizant client. With that said, this chapter is not a substitute for advanced training in verbal psychotherapy. In its basic form it provides for the novice therapist skills within a framework for verbal interaction based from the music experience. Many of these techniques will help the client clarify basic issues that are arising from the music experience and provide for the music therapist added tools in their repertoire of techniques.

The knowledge that is gleaned from these techniques can ultimately be communicated to the treatment team as additional information relating to the progress of the client resulting from the music therapy experience.

REFERENCES

Borczon, R.M. (1997). *Music Therapy: Group vignettes.* Gilsum, NH: Barcelona Publishers.

Egan, G. (1982). *The skilled helper.* Belmont, CA: Wadsworth, Inc.

Hanser, S. (1999). *The new music therapist's handbook.* (2nd Ed.). Boston, MA: Berklee Press.

Kennedy, E. and Charles, S. (2001). *On becoming a counselor.* NY, NY: The Crossroad Publishing Company.

Martin, D.G. (1989). *Counseling and therapy skills.* Prospect Heights Il: Waveland Press, Inc.

Chapter 5

INTERVENTION STRATEGIES FOR THE DIFFICULT CLIENT

By
Ronald Borczon, MT-BC
Kasi Peters, MT-BC
Lesa MacEwan, MT-TBC
Erin Salez, MT-BC

Through the course of undergraduate study, you read about the many success stories that have come through music therapy sessions. From this knowledge you come to believe, and many times expect, that within your sessions the same level of success will consistently occur. When these positive events do occur it reaffirms for you the effectiveness of music therapy as well as your own feelings about your abilities.

However, when a client comes in having a "bad day," or events occur that are seemingly negative in nature, you are faced with a possible series of behaviors/attitudes which you are neither expecting nor entirely ready to handle. If the client, by his/her very nature, has problems severe enough to be confrontational, aggressive, non-responsive, or in various ways resistive, you may not understand (except in theory) the application of various approaches to deal with the client's behavior. In these instances you may feel frustrated and lost as to what to say or do.

For the purposes of this chapter, the client is defined as a child who currently has a diagnosis that places him/her into the general category of "special needs" and whose diagnosis would lend him/her to be included in the general definition of "The Individuals with Disabilities Education Act Amendments of 1997," which states:

> "The term 'child with a disability' means a child with mental retardation, hearing impairments (including deafness), speech or language impairments, visual impairments (including blindness), serious emotional disturbance (hereinafter referred

to as emotional disturbance), orthopedic impairments, autism, traumatic brain injury, or other health impairments, or specific learning disabilities; and who, by reason thereof, needs special education and related services."

The general concept of the "difficult" client is better defined by the various behaviors that are cited in the numerous examples in this chapter. The framework of the chapter considers that the client is involved in a music therapy intervention, but because of and/or through various behaviors, the client is disengaging from the intervention. The reasons for the disengagement or underlying pathology may be alluded to in the description, but generally are not the subject matter of this discourse. To become involved in this dialogue may distract from the purpose of this chapter. Care must be taken to understand the diagnosis and individual behaviors of each client. Because of the variations of success that we see in attempting to re-engage a client who is disengaging from or exhibiting resistance to a music therapy intervention, we must build a repertoire of approaches and strategies. This repertoire is best established through experience, practice, video evaluation of self/client, and *not* using this chapter verbatim, but using it as a guide. Work on the understanding of the subtleties of the approaches and techniques offered and become proficient in the adaptation of these approaches. These approaches are not always behavior-specific, and they often can be used in many situations. All in all, these techniques serve as an excellent starting point in working with a difficult client.

The categories that follow and the approaches that are given have been drawn from observations of various clients and clinicians in the California State University, Northridge Music Therapy Wellness Clinic and are by no means all-inclusive. They are based on behaviors and interventions that have been generally seen over four months of clinical observation. Additionally, it is important to emphasize that these approaches are not ranked in order of priority. They are, in fact, placed in no particular order, as some might be quite inappropriate for certain clients. These strategies must be applied judiciously based on your knowledge of the client and the situation at hand.

> If a client is resisting and/or being
> disruptive, try to take into consideration
> what is going on with the client.

The term "reinforce" will be used in various places. When used, it is referring to a sincere response (acknowledgement) by the therapist to the client. To "reinforce" the client is to affirm to the client that he/she has done something that is appropriate and is in his/her best interest. There are many times throughout the chapter where there is no specific mention of reinforcement. It is assumed that you have assimilated this technique into your repertory of responses and are well versed in the appropriate use and manner of reinforcement. In fact, as a rule, *know that immediate reinforcement of the appropriate response/behavior should be present in all examples and techniques to follow.*

Within given behaviors there are emotional components. A general rule of thumb in working with all clients who are resisting and/or being disruptive is to try to understand and take into consideration what is going on with the client. Do not take their resistance personally. Quite often in reviewing the videotape where such behavior is occurring, the question should be proffered, "What is this client trying to tell me?" Even though the handbook is primarily dealing with overt behavior and techniques for that behavior, there is always the underlying purpose that we may often not understand, but still need to consider.

SITUATIONS AND APPROACHES

If the Client Exhibits Off-Task Behavior

During the course of a session the client may go off-task. Off-task is defined as the time when a client appears to be attending to internal or external stimuli that keep him/her from focusing on the current activity or task at hand. When this occurs there are several possible interventions that the music therapist can utilize.

Situation 1: Client is involved in counting activity within a melody to a song. The music therapist is playing chords on the piano and encouraging the client to recognize and count numbers on a sheet that are also contained in the lyrics. The client begins to look away and seems disengaged.

Approaches:

- Say client's name, then reinforce when client re-engages.
- Stop music until client pays attention, then resume with the music.
- Verbal encouragement to the task at hand without song or music.
- Ask client to participate in activity.

Situation 2: During singing activities, the client begins offering off-topic information regarding his day at school.

Approaches:

- Incorporate suggestions or verbal encouragement into song lyrics. For example: As you're singing/playing song, add client's name and what you would like him/her to do, i.e., to "Row Your Boat"…replace with "Billy play the drum, oh so quietly!"
- Change voice that you're singing in such as: Squeaky mouse voice; Crabby crab voice; Big Daddy low booming voice; Elvis.
- Stop the music, let the client finish, then begin back with the music.

Situation 3: During instrument playing, the client suddenly stops playing and looks away from the music therapist.

Approaches:

- Use a new stimulus to gain attention so that you might guide client back to activity, for example: Glissando on piano or xylophone.
- Change dynamics of music (loud to soft or soft to loud).
- Change register of instrument or change instrument.
- Change position of instrument (i.e., hold the snare drum up high), therefore creating a sense of excitement and anticipation.
- Follow or direct client to new instrument and attempt to engage.
- Continue with activity and be patient.

- Physically guide client back to activity.
- Use cadence of music to cue participation.

If the Client Resists a New Instrument and Tantrums

Often clients who demonstrate resistive behaviors are doing so in response to a change in comfort level or familiarity. Tantrums and other behaviors may occur when the music therapist introduces a novel instrument, activity or song. The client may also exhibit tantrum-like behaviors if the room is not set up in a familiar manner. As a therapist, it is important to assess the reason(s) why the tantrum may be occurring and whether a simple change can be made to provide comfort or a shift for the client.

> *Situation 1:* The client has just entered the music therapy room to begin the session. The music therapist has set up the room so that there is one new instrument sitting amongst the other familiar instruments. The client sees the instrument and begins crying out, "No..."
> *Approaches:*
> - Leave instrument in visual proximity for 2-3 sessions before using musically.
> - Acknowledge that the instrument is new.
> - Take it away immediately.
> - Model playing the instrument and attempt a hand-over-hand technique (place your hand underneath the client's hand to direct him as to how to play the instrument).
>
> *Situation 2 :*In a group setting, one client chooses an instrument that has never been played before, and one or more of the other group members becomes upset and tantrums.
> *Approaches:*
> - Sing a song about a "new and different instrument."
> - Acknowledge fear with a simple "I know, it's new."
> - Attempt to have the client share the instrument with other members.

Situation 3: During the session, the music therapist presents a new instrument to the client, which results in the client resisting playing the instrument and getting boisterous.

Approaches:

- Move instrument farther away from him/her.
- Tell client to take his/her time to get used to the look or sound of the instrument.
- Compare instrument to something he/she likes and is familiar with (for example shapes, colors, and/or familiar objects).

If the Client is Involved in "Self-Stimulating" Behaviors

Self-stimulating behaviors may interfere with the clients' ability to attend or participate in a meaningful way. Some of these "stimming" behaviors can be spinning, flapping, or rocking. Stimming on instruments can also be exhibited, such as perseverating (redundant or non-purposeful repetition of word(s) or action(s) without progression) on the beads of a cabasa. Try to find a way to either break the pattern or support the stimulating behavior through your music therapy intervention. By supporting this behavior you can build a bridge of communication with the client at their level and eventually may be able to direct him/her out of the behavior through the music.

Situation 1: During a piano improvisation, the client begins perseverating on two notes, repeating them over and over without regard to musical accompaniment and demonstrating inflexibility in his rhythm and pattern.

Approaches:

- Join the client in his/her rhythms and patterns, then attempt to move away musically from the pattern and encourage the client to do the same.
- Slow your rhythms in an attempt to slow the client's rhythms.
- Alter your rhythm in an attempt to get "in between" his/her notes on the piano in order to break his/her pattern.

Situation 2: While participating in a drumming activity with the music therapist, the client stops drumming and begins flicking the mallets in front of his/her eyes.

Approaches:

- Invite client to play or get involved with a new instrument.
- Provide a stimulus for an incompatible response. The definition of an incompatible response is a behavior that by its very nature cannot exist while another behavior is exhibited. For example, if a client is prone to put his hand in his mouth, engage the client in holding a mallet and drumming. The two cannot exist at the same time.
- Reinforce any appropriate behavior that breaks the pattern of the self-stimulatory behavior.

Situation 3: During the music therapy session, the music therapist presents the client with claves. The client immediately begins repetitively playing the claves up against his ear and demonstrating resistance toward using them in any other manner.

Approaches:

- Join in and structure the perseveration. Make it musical and at some point introduce the client to a new sound or instrument.
- Ask for a turn in order to make it a social experience.
- Ask the client to tell you "how many more times" he's going to do the behavior.

If the Client Walks Away
From the Music Therapist

Your client has walked away before, during, or after a music therapy intervention. Is there a way to entice the client to return to the intervention through musical strategies? You may feel a verbal cue might be the appropriate method for re-engaging the client as well. It is important to determine why the client is removing himself from the situation. Is it a new intervention? This may be difficult for some clients; therefore, you may want to introduce your intervention gradually. Is the client bored? Have you changed the way you have typically presented an intervention? Is the music too loud? Is something visually over-stimulating? Does the client need a break or need space? Assessing the client's behavior is as important as assessing yourself and the music therapy setting.

Situation 1: Upon initiating a xylophone improvisation, the client immediately walks away.
Approaches:
- Continue with music until client returns.
- Stop playing until client returns.
- Sing a song asking or instructing client to come back to activity.
- Verbally redirect the client by requesting that he return to the activity, for example, by singing the client's name to the melody of the song and singing what you would like the client to do:
  "It would sound so much nicer if you were playing too."
  "Which instrument will you play next?"
  "Can you think of a different way to play that?"
- Incorporate client's actions into song lyrics.

Situation 2: In a group setting during a familiar activity, one group member leaves the group area.
Approaches:
- Set up the room to your advantage by setting up clear boundaries for the musical space.
- If in a group, have another client play and ask him/her what he/she thinks of other client's playing.

Situation 3: After 5 minutes of active participation in one activity, the client stands up and walks away prior to the completion of the activity.

Approaches:
- Allow the client to walk away (know when to give them space).
- If the above is the case, keep the music going, as this may bring the client back.
- Create a song about walking.
- Depending on level of client functioning, establish a contingency such as telling the client that he/she needs to do

activity for ____ amount of times/minutes and then they can do another activity.

- Stop the activity - it might be appropriate to let it go, especially if it is frustrating the client.

Situation 4: At the beginning of the session, the client walks around the room and away from the music therapist. He does not show interest in the therapist or any instruments placed in the room.
Approaches:

- Approach client and imitate any sounds the client is making.
- Physically guide client back to activity or instrument.
- Tell the client they must return to the area.

If the Client Begins Vocalizing "Upset Sounds" or Crying

After assessing the components of the music therapy session that may be affecting the client, it may also be helpful to determine whether the client entered the session in distress. When appropriate, ask the client why he is upset. If your view is that every response is a valid response and that gives you information about the client, it is necessary to validate and acknowledge your client's feelings. How can you support your client's feelings through music therapy interventions? Perhaps the client needs to cry and your role must be simply to musically support this expression, listen, and hear.

Situation 1: The client arrives at the music therapy session upset and crying. The music therapist is not aware of the antecedent condition or how long the client has been upset.
Approaches:

- Respond to vocalizations in a conversational manner, for example, using a call and response format. When the client vocalizes, the therapist may respond with a vocalization or with words that move in the opposite direction from the client's original vocalization.
- Continue with imitations of sounds as a way to validate client's expressions.

- Gradually try to change the crying into singing.
- Acknowledge feelings.
- Present an instrument that is enjoyable and familiar and begin to play it.
- When appropriate, ask the client, "What's wrong?"
- Create a song about moods and use it so that it becomes a familiar part of the session. Then use it when the client exhibits any of the moods from the song.

Situation 2: The client becomes upset and cries when his/her parent/caregiver leaves the room.
Approaches:
- Give verbal responses as opposed to encouraging vocalizations as an alternative to using words, i.e., narrate the feelings for the client by saying, "I'm feeling sad right now, etc."
- Provide comfort via musical or verbal explanation, i.e., "Mommy comes back in a few minutes."

Situation 3: After the music therapist has explained rules regarding instrument care to the client (for example, regarding not being allowed to detune the guitar pegs), the client breaks the rules and becomes upset and begins crying.
Approaches:
- Sing a song about antecedent condition, i.e., "Sometimes it's hard to remember the rules and when I forget, I feel sad."
- Ask the client if he/she has anything to say.

Situation 4: While actively participating in a music activity, the client suddenly begins crying out and making "upset sounds."
Approaches:
- Assess the situation to check for pain.
- Is something familiar missing? If so, bring it back in to the environment.
- Is the music too loud or soft? If so, correct the volume.
- Determine whether the client has dropped something or is in need of something.

In many of these instances the client needs to find a sense of calmness. Useful approaches for calming the client include, but are not limited to:

- Matching the client's current affect musically, and gradually slowing the tempo and mood down.
- Use breathing techniques for relaxation: i.e., Inhale 4 beats, hold 4 beats, exhale 4 beats.
- Play music that closely matches a typical heart rate and perform slow, fluid, gross motor movements with the client (swaying, bending, stretching, etc.)
- Play a slow, steady beat on a large drum and have the client match your playing in order to focus. Gradually slow the tempo down.
- Perform descending, legato vocal glissandos on vowel sounds (add gross motor movements to match, if needed.)

If the Client Attempts to Throw or Drop Instruments in a Playful Manner

Oftentimes, the clients we are working with are just beginning to develop a sense of themselves and their impact on the world around them. They are often developing an understanding of the concept of cause and effect, which results in the client's participating in actions that produce a large response from the therapist. (Think of a toddler who often drops his spoon or toys from his highchair to develop a game with his mother of "dropping and picking up.") Also, clients may be testing the therapist to see just how much they can get away with. It is important to set limits while providing positive instructions that allow the client to successfully stay within the limits.

> *Situation 1:* While playing the hello song, the client picks up instruments, drops them on the floor and laughs.
> *Approaches:*
> - Hold one end of instrument with the client so that it doesn't hit the floor.
> - Hold instrument while the client plays it.

- Imitate same throwing motion as the client while continuing to hold the mallets; instead of throwing, make the same motion while playing the instrument.
- Have client use hands instead of mallets.
- Verbally redirect the client toward another instrument.
- Have only the instruments that are a necessity.
- Require client to pick up equipment before continuing activity.

Situation 2: While participating in a beanbag passing song with the music therapist and parent, the client throws the beanbag instead of passing it and laughs while looking from the music therapist to her mother.
Approaches:
- Replace the object with something else.
- Create a limit, through lyrics, that lets the client know not to throw the instruments.
- Say, "no throwing," or "hold it tight," before the object leaves the client's hands (catch and stop the behavior before it happens) and reinforce the appropriate behavior.

Situation 3: During a dance and freeze song that incorporates egg shakers, the client consistently drops the egg shakers when he freezes, and laughs.
Approaches:
- Physically stop and redirect the throwing action.
- Firmly give a verbal redirection, "No throwing the instruments."
- Stop the music and tell the client that it might be too hard to use that instrument today and put it away.

Situation 4: After 5 minutes of actively participating in a music activity, the client begins dropping the instruments and laughing.
Approaches:
- Make a new instrument inviting by creating a sense of urgency for the client to participate.
- If the client is throwing smaller instruments, keep those out of reach or out of the music area.

If the Client Won't Begin the Activity

Whether facilitating a new or a familiar music therapy intervention, you may find you have sessions in which your client will not enter into an intervention/session. If it is a new intervention, it is important to respect that your client may need some tools for transition. How can you add a familiar nuance to your new intervention for your client? Likewise, when engaging in a familiar intervention with which the client may, be bored, how can you add a new component in order to spark your client's interest? It is helpful to know your client in order to create music therapy interventions that are at his/her level and that are maximally deferential to his preferences, likes, and dislikes. Having full knowledge of your client can be a powerful cache for you to utilize to assist in engaging and sustaining your client's interests.

Situation 1: During the hello song, the client remains standing at the door and will not join the therapist in the designated music space and does not participate in the hello song.
Approaches:
- Encourage client to play "one time."
- Ask client to participate.
- Offer a choice between activities.
- Offer choice of playing different instruments.

Situation 2: During group music games, the client will not participate in his turn, or simply sits quietly throughout the activity.
Approaches:
- Say client's name and, "Play!" (in an upbeat voice).
- Provide verbal encouragement.
- Allow client to watch until comfortable to join, and acknowledge that, "It's okay to wait and watch."
- Playfully use preparatory words and music such as, "It's nearly time to…" or "Get ready to…" and other frequent use phrases such as, "Ready, Set, Go," or "1, 2, 3…"

If the Client Exhibits Aggressive Behavior

Behaviors can be communicative in intent. When a client exhibits aggressive behavior, it is important to assess what the client is communicating. Is the client frustrated because the music therapy intervention is too difficult? Is the sound of the instrument you have chosen painful? Did the client exhibit these behaviors in other settings during the day and/or has there been a medication change? While there are a plethora of questions you can ask which can be related or unrelated to your particular intervention, it is crucial that you keep yourself protected at all times during music therapy sessions whether or not your client has previously exhibited these behaviors. It is equally imperative not to personalize your client's behavior, only to assess the communication and underlying purpose.

Situation 1: During a music activity involving instruments, the client kicks the guitar as it sits on its stand.
Approaches:
- Redirect the client.
- Verbally tell client that the behavior is inappropriate, i.e., "That's not okay."
- If it persists, terminate the session.

Situation 2: While sitting at the piano with the music therapist, the client leans over to bite the therapist on the arm.
Approaches:
- Stay calm and assess the situation.
- Protect yourself at all times.
- Involve parent or co-therapist.
- Don't get angry or escalate the situation.
- Tell the client that this behavior is not allowed.
- Try to determine the antecedent of the behavior so that you will be better prepared in the future.

Situation 3: While drumming, the client attempts to or participates in the motions of hitting the music therapist with the mallets.
Approaches:
- Utilize music that matches the energy of the client and redirect him/her into the musical experience.
- Model appropriate behaviors, i.e., demonstrate hitting the drum, not people, with the mallet.
- Alter tone of voice and affect to reflect seriousness of behavior. Redirect into a positive experience.

If the Client Hits

Because many facilities are considered to be "hands off," meaning that there should be no aggressive physical contact between a client and staff, it is important to be aware of deflection and redirection techniques when dealing with physically violent clients.

Situation: A 7-year-old girl with severe emotional behavioral disorders is participating in her weekly music therapy session when she becomes frustrated and attempts to hit the therapist.
Approaches:
- Stay calm and attempt to deflect or redirect the hitting motion away from you.
- If you are unable to deflect the motion, verbally tell the client that hitting is not okay or allowed.
- If the situation escalates, involve a parent or secondary therapist.
- Try to understand why the client is hitting. If you are videotaping the session, review the tape to determine what the antecedents to the negative behavior were.
- Don't suppress the client's need to do something. In this case, hitting is the physical manifestation of the client's need to release anger or frustration. Give the client an opportunity to do this more appropriately.
- Be prepared to document the incident according to your facility's policies.

If the Client Expresses Verbal Intention of Violence

Before starting to work with clients who pose a potential threat or who have histories of violent behaviors, become fully versed with your facility's policies. Does working with this population require additional professional assault training? Does the facility require special documentation when a conflict or aggressive behavior is acted upon? Know your surroundings and who to call when in need of help.

If a client verbally expresses an intention of violence, either toward you, another individual in the room, or to themselves, remain calm. Panicking will only increase the energy and tension in the room, as well as cloud your judgment. Survey your immediate environment. What is available to the client that may potentially be used as a weapon?

> *Situation:* During the music therapy session the client verbalizes the desire to hit or hurt someone.
> *Approaches:*
> - Acknowledge the client's emotion. "Those are very strong feelings you are having."
> - Let the client know that the result of acting out the desire could be painful. "If you hit me, that would hurt."
> - Explain that there are different ways of letting out the anger. "Because it's not okay to go around hitting people without consequences, we have to come up with another way to let that anger out." "Show me what your anger sounds like," or, "What does your anger sound like?"
> - Talk about consequences if the action is followed through.
> - Don't attempt to out-shout the client if he/she is using a loud voice.

If the Client is Fidgety or Bouncing in His Chair

There will be times when you are working with a client who cannot or will not remain still. He/she may fidget, rock or bounce in his/her chair, wander around the room or fidget with instruments in a non-purposeful manner. These behaviors may be self-stimulating in nature or they may be a result of excitement, being upset, boredom, or may be used as a coping mechanism in order for him/her to be able to focus. For example, there are many children who are unable to focus unless they are fidgeting or moving some part of their body. It is important to assess possible reasons why the behavior is occurring prior to requesting that the child sit still. Once you have some ideas about why the fidgeting is occurring, there are several techniques that may work to increase the client's involvement in the activity or intervention.

Situation 1: During a book singing activity, the client constantly bounces up and down in his chair.
Approaches:
- Invite the client to conduct the activity.
- Provide sensory stimulation, if needed, i.e. deep pressure, jumping, etc.
- Find the rhythm in the bounce and incorporate that rhythm into the activity. Try to redirect the energy into a positive musical experience.

Situation 2: During group activities, one group member constantly moves from seat to seat and around the room without staying in one place for the duration of an activity.
Approaches:
- Do an activity that involves fast movement and gradually decrease tempo.
- Incorporate an activity that involves gross motor movement.
- Use a body-awareness activity to increase client's spatial awareness and sense of self.

Situation 3: While the music therapist is introducing an activity to the client, the client continuously, aimlessly and non-musically touches all the instruments.
Approaches:
- Use an activity in which the client has to listen to or pick out certain words or instrument sounds (to increase attention to task).

- Set up instruments around the room and develop an activity that involves playing the instruments in a sequence while moving around the room.

If the Client Grabs the Instrument and Runs

Situation: Client and music therapist are engaged in a musical improvisation at the piano when the client reaches up, grabs a horn and proceeds to run around the room.
Approaches:
- Stop the music until the client returns to the music therapy area.
- Position yourself in front of the client, secure the instrument and attempt to calm him/her. By positioning yourself in front of the client, you eliminate a power struggle where the client is leading you around the room.
- Create a song about running back to the appropriate place.

If the Client Begins Hitting Table/Wall

Situation 1: Kyle, an 8-year-old boy with autism, is seated opposite the music therapist with a large gathering drum between the two. He has successfully played the drum with the therapist for 30 seconds when he reaches up and begins to hit the wall with his mallet.
Approaches:
- Verbally redirect the client to bring him back to the activity.
- In an upbeat voice say, "Kyle, play the drum."
- Stop the music. Oftentimes the cessation of accompanying music will be enough to bring the client back to the here and now, then attempt to re-engage the client in the activity.
- Present another instrument for the client to play.
- While maintaining a steady beat on the gathering drum, pick up a smaller instrument and hold it towards the client. Verbally redirect the client to play the new instrument. By providing the client with a new stimulus, you are creating an interesting and engaging way to return to the present and continue with the activity.

- Be familiar with the instruments and styles of music that the client finds soothing, calming and engaging; present one of those choices to him.
- If you want to discourage the act of hitting, present the client with an instrument that requires a more gentle touch.

If the Client Stops Participating in the Activity

Situation 1: A 12-year-old girl with Downs Syndrome is playing temple blocks, and is seated next to the music therapist at the piano. After playing for two minutes, the client stops participating.
Approaches:
- Assess whether the activity is not challenging enough or too challenging for the client's level of functioning.
- If the activity is too challenging, use hand over hand motions by either placing your hand on top of or underneath the client's hand. Continue playing an ostinato or moving bass line on the piano using your available hand, or discontinue use of piano for duration of activity.
- If activity is not challenging enough, improvise out of the structure. Perhaps engage the client in a call and response activity for a few bars by having her copy a rhythmic patter you play on the piano or vice versa. Return to the original structure to provide the client with consistency.

Situation 2: Client is often obstinate in behavior. He/she is doing this as part of a manipulation or power struggle.
Approaches:
- Continue the activity without the client.
- Invite him/her to continue a little more and then stop quickly after he/she joins in, thanking him/her for coming back into the music. Then change activity.
- Determine whether the client wishes to do something else. At this juncture, you can stop the activity and begin a new one or let the client know that she needs to complete the activity for _x_ amount of times before being able to move on.

If the Client Continues to Talk During the Activity

Clients who consistently talk during a session may be experiencing some level of discomfort or nervousness. Talking often becomes the tangible manifestation of feelings of anxiety. The client may have had an exciting or traumatic day and has the need to share the experience with someone they trust. However, the client may also use talking as a diversionary tactic. Perhaps he/she does not want to participate in music therapy and begins talking in order to stall the session.

> *Situation 1:* An 8-year-old boy with severe emotional behavior disorders and Attention Deficit Disorder with Hyperactivity attends music therapy weekly and is engaged in playing the keyboard with the therapist when he begins to talk about his friend and loses focus on the music.
> *Approaches:*
> - Ignore the talking and encourage the client to continue playing the keyboard. Invite client to participate while ignoring the talking.
> - If the client continues to talk about his friend and other kids at school, determine whether the client is simply bored with the activity.
> - Ask the client if he would like to finish this activity in order to move on. "Let's finish this song on the piano and you can choose what we do next." This gives the client a sense of autonomy and allows him to be responsible for a choice.
> - Improvise out of the activity and create a song about his day at school and his friends.

> *Situation 2:* A 10-year-old girl, Julia, with severe emotional behavioral disorders attends music therapy weekly and is consistent in her ability to focus on given tasks through to completion. Julia enters the room and appears distraught. She sits down at the piano but begins to talk rather than engage in music. She mentions an event that has distressed her.

In this situation, where the client is obviously emotionally distressed about a traumatic situation, it would be inappropriate to ignore the behavior. If you were to ignore the behavior, you run the risk of alienating the client and give her the sense that adults do not take her seriously.

Approaches:
- Tell the client that it seems as though something important happened and give her the opportunity to share the event.
- Turn the event into a song that helps the client express feelings.

If the Client is Playing the Instrument Too Harshly

Situation: A 5-year-old is drumming with the music therapist when he becomes excited during the activity and begins to play the instrument more aggressively.

Approaches:
- If the behavior is inappropriate and disruptive to the session, ask the client to play more gently.
- Make a game out of playing different dynamics. Take the "harsh" playing and make a loud drum "rumble" out of it, moving to a soft drum "rumble," alternating back and forth in an engaging manner.
- When appropriate, re-establish a basic ground beat and move on with the activity.
- If the client is playing the instrument harshly due to a lack of motor control, change the type of mallet to lessen the sound of the instrument and/or model appropriate playing of the instrument.
- If the client is being genuinely inappropriate and continues playing aggressively, discontinue the activity and provide the client with the opportunity to do something else.

If the Client is Constantly Questioning

Situation 1: Joe, a 13-year-old boy, is in a music therapy group with six other teenagers. Joe interrupts the group process by asking if the therapist has ever played a certain video game.
Approaches:

- Ignore the question.
- Let the client know that the question will be answered when the activity is over. "Joe, right now isn't an appropriate time to discuss that. We'll talk about it when group is over." Be sure to follow through and answer the client's question when you say you will.

Situation 2: Four children are participating in a hello/greeting song, playing small percussion instruments and taking turns soloing. One client, Amy, begins asking where Marc is.
Approaches:

- Ignore the question and continue with the song.
- Answer the question and redirect back to the music. "Marc isn't here. Amy, tell me who should play next?"
- Make the client's participation in the music essential. "Amy, it's your turn to solo! Let's hear it!"

SUMMARY

This chapter offers various approaches to working with children who have "special needs" and are not actively participating in the music therapy with "on task" or appropriate behavior. While many techniques are offered, these approaches are not exclusive to their examples. They can be used in various situations and are not meant to be the only way to handle such behaviors. Rather, these approaches are meant to serve as a starting point in the development of your style regarding how to engage and work with a person exhibiting behaviors that are offered in the examples.

As each client is different, so must be techniques used. When you notice that a client responds well to an approach, keep it in mind for the next time the behavior occurs. Don't be surprised, however, if it doesn't work every single time.

Two very important concepts are mentioned in this chapter: The ability to reinforce and affirm immediately the client's appropriate behavior, and the fact that this behavior cannot become about you and your concept of self-worth. The authors of this chapter are firm believers in the idea that, while a client may exhibit inappropriate behaviors during a session, the client should be given immediate positive feedback after engaging in any desired behavior or response. This feedback needs to be specific to the behavior/response and above all, sincere.

When things are not going according to plan, keep the focus on the client. Do not get into a thought pattern about your own skills failing in the moment as this will distract you from the task at hand. While the client may be reacting to something that you have done, it does not necessarily mean you did the wrong thing. The client is reacting to an event. This moment is not the best time to review what you did, but rather what are you going to do. With supervision and possible review of videotape you can try to understand the antecedent of the incident if you feel it was related to something you did. In many instances it is not what "we" did as music therapists, it is "what is going on" in that moment for the client that causes him/her to disengage.

Chapter 6

DOCUMENTATION

THE PROCESS

Documentation is a required aspect of any therapy. Through this process a written record occurs that traces the history of the client up to and through your interaction with him/her. This process of documentation can and often does begin prior to ever having seen the client. This process starts with what is known as a "referral."

Referral

The referral for music therapy services can come from a variety of sources. In most clinical settings it comes from another professional such as a physician, social worker, psychologist, teacher, occupational therapist, recreational therapist, speech and language pathologist, physical therapist, art therapist, counselors, or any other professional that has the ability to recommend music therapy as the treatment modality. Parents may also refer children, and clients can also refer themselves. If an interdisciplinary team is involved in the planning of treatment, the team may recommend music therapy for the client. The referral is done in writing via a "referral form." This form is unique to each employing agency and/or private practice. It gives a brief look at the client and includes their age, sex, medications, and other relevant information. The form usually includes a statement as to why this client is being referred to music therapy.

Assessment

Once a referral has been given the next step is the "assessment." The assessment is completed prior to the actual treatment process. In its basic form it can be thought of as a "tool" that gathers information regarding what the client is able to do and not able to do. Another way to think of it is that through this tool, you are able to see the strengths and weaknesses of the client. Each discipline usually does its own assessment and the more information you can gather about the client the better informed you are about his/her total capability. Asking for assessment summaries from other disciplines (e.g. speech therapy, physical therapy, social services, etc.) is often helpful.

In the field of music therapy, the assessment process continues to develop within the profession. As music overlaps with other disciplines you're often looking at non-musical behaviors and responses that are also areas of concern for your particular population, thus formal assessments are population specific. For example, in working with an adolescent who is diagnosed with conduct disorder, the assessment may differ in several areas from that of an adolescent of the same age, who is severely developmentally delayed. Similarly, the adolescent's assessment would be different in many ways from that of a geriatric patient. In looking at musical behaviors in any assessment, however, common ground can be found in client's responses to the elements of music such as tone/pitch, timbre, style, texture, harmony, and rhythm. Other areas that can be looked at are the ability to play instruments, reactions to instruments, and preferences for certain instruments.

Along with aiding in the identification of strong and weak characteristics of the client, the data gleaned from the assessment also serves as a baseline from which to chart the progress of the client. From this assessment, goals and objectives are established and the movement towards these is routinely measured against the baseline.

> Music therapy assessments find a
> common ground in client's responses to
> and involvement with the music.

Treatment Plan

Evolving out of the assessment is the "treatment plan." Through the assessment, the areas that need to be addressed have been discovered and, via the treatment plan, these areas are listed and prioritized. If there is a "treatment team" involved, as there is in most settings, the team will often have an active role in the development of the treatment plan. The composition of the treatment team varies (much like the assessment) depending on the site and population. Generally speaking it is comprised of those professionals who are intricately involved in the treatment of the client. The treatment team identifies general goals and assigns these to appropriate disciplines. Thus, the assigning of goals comes to the music therapist via a "referral" by the treatment team and is often accompanied by projected timelines regarding the achievement of specific target goals.

   If you are in a private practice and are not part of a Treatment Team per se, you start with the referral, followed by the music therapy assessment, then develop the goals and treatment plan.

Goals and Objectives

   While the goals and objectives for the client are intricately related, they are vastly different in presentation and function. Goals are general statements regarding where the client should be heading in the treatment. The goal statements are long-term results that the client will hopefully achieve. The objectives, however, specify an expected result. They are building blocks in the process of reaching a goal. They are the behavioral verification that defines the goal and are the guideposts through which progress is measured in therapy. With that being said, goals and objectives are defined below.

Goal – a broad or general statement of direction of a behavior or emotional state to be achieved.

Objective – a specific observable behavior that leads to an intended goal. The behavior is verifiable within a given time and under specific conditions.

> While the goals and objectives for the client are intricately related, they are vastly different in presentation and function.

Writing a good objective is imperative in planning the treatment strategy and evaluating the progress of the client. With clear and specific statements it becomes easier to identify whether the client is actually making progress through music therapy treatment.

The specificity of the objective has many different levels. In learning how to write an objective, the following specific points are to be considered:

What behavior will the client do? This refers to the observable behavior that the client will accomplish or demonstrate. It is expressed in the action verb of the sentence. For example: The client *will sing three notes, C,D and E...*

When will the client do it? This refers to various types of conditions, some that are givens and some that need identification. Conditions can be related to time – when will the behavior be completed; a program condition – such as during the music therapy session; or a condition under which certain behaviors are to be assessed such as after a cue or prompt.

What is the performance level to be achieved and how is it measured. It is necessary to have a standard that is the acceptable level of accomplishment in order to continue the movement toward the stated goal that the objective is drawn from. The measurement of the specified behavior can be of various methods such as counted, compared, listed in percentage, and listed in relationship to a time line.

These divisions of an objective do not necessarily need to follow a certain order. As long as these are all clearly stated within the objective, the statement should be able to stand alone.

Below is an example of a goal and an objective. For illustrative purposes the client will be an 85-year-old man in a nursing facility.

> Goal: Increase socialization.
> Objective: Grandpa Aaron will initiate saying hello to at least 3 other participants in the choir during the first 3 minutes of the music therapy session.

Now let us take a look at why this is a good objective. First in looking at the goal, it stated that an "increase" in socialization is required. There are many behaviors that fall under socialization such as talking to someone else, shaking hands with another person, etc. The objective is a small, targeted behavior that is a step in the direction of increasing socialization as a goal.

> The clearer the objective is,
> the easier it is to structure the
> implementation of the
> music therapy intervention.

Below the objective is restated, and cited in italics are important observations regarding the objective.

> Objective: Grandpa Aaron *(who is listed – the client is referred to by name, which is not a requirement but it is illustrative for this example. Often just using the term "the client" is enough as*

the objective is being written in the chart, or for insertion in the chart.) will initiate saying hello to at least 3 other participants *(This is the action to be performed – note that the requirement is to "initiate" rather than respond to. This places responsibility on the client for the action. Three participants is a random number, it might be more appropriate to have it be a single participant depending on Grandpa Aaron's level of functioning. The number of participants listed is also the measurement to be achieved along with the following.)* in the choir during the first 3 minutes of the music therapy session. *(Thus the conditions are given as a time line and in what setting.)*

In looking at the example you can see that it is clear as to who is performing what, when it is occurring, and to what specific degree it is to occur.

The clearer the objective is, the easier it is to structure the implementation of the music therapy intervention. This clarity also enables proper data collection for subsequent reporting. The writing of a clear and accurate objective is crucial to the overall process of documentation.

Treatment

The development of the music therapy treatment strategy and its subsequent implementation is the core of what separates the field of music therapy from all other therapies. Being trained as a music therapist means that you have the ability to look at any goal, develop music-based treatment strategy, and through its implementation, aid the client in his/her progress. The development of the treatment strategy must always begin with this question: "How do I help the client achieve this goal through music?" This line of thinking puts into motion a chain reaction of previous learning, intuition, and philosophical orientation. Initially, the inexperienced therapist should outline various ideas that are then internalized as part of his/her style. These ideas are then easily called upon and further explored in the music therapy setting.

While in the session, there is an evaluation process that you must be internally experiencing regarding the events that are occurring. Being "present" for the client and making necessary adjustments in the moment can help the client move forward in the therapeutic process. During this process of assessing the intervention strategy, its subsequent evolution, and the evaluation of client behaviors, any movement toward the objective(s) needs to be noted and/or recorded. This gathering of data for the purpose of documenting progress is crucial to the evolution of the treatment and development of the client.

> As a music therapist you can take any goal and develop a music-based treatment strategy to achieve it.

THE PURPOSE OF DATA COLLECTION

There are several reasons why music therapists must be able to document the progress of a client in a coherent and professional manner. First of all, institutions are required to keep records of the client. This is often done as a chronology and allows for an easy review of the history of the client while in the facility or in treatment. The book (or the place of collection) where all this information is held is commonly known as the "chart." The documentation that is provided by the music therapist will have a special place in the chart that is pre-determined by the institution providing the treatment.

A second reason for data collection is that it is an effective means by which professionals can communicate about the client without having to meet face-to-face which is often difficult in the day-to-day operation of an institution. The notes in the chart let others know what occurred in the session and can give valuable information about the state of the client for that day.

Third, the actual progress of the client is monitored as well as the effectiveness of a modality. The documentation should be geared to addressing the goals/objectives that are assigned to your particular discipline, as this is the primary reason the client is in your treatment modality. While your documentation is to be focused on the assigned objective, it is appropriate to list any significant events (outside of the goal) that may provide valuable information to others regarding the overall development of the client. For example, if you are working with a child reproducing simple phonemes who has cerebral palsy, the child might not be doing too well on achieving the vocal objectives for the day, but he/she does reach up, grab a drumstick, and play the drum. This may be something he/she has never done before, and you may have knowledge that another goal (not assigned to music therapy) is to grasp an object and hold it. This would certainly be worth documenting and is relevant to the development of the child.

Fourth, if there is an insurance company that is paying for the client's treatment, it may want to see the notes in order to determine whether the client is making progress. The company may review the notes so as to see their accuracy in addressing the rationale for the client's treatment. If a client is excelling towards the goals in the music therapy session, a well written music therapy note can often serve as a justification for the use of music therapy in helping the client achieve the goals set forth in the treatment plan.

And fifth, this document that is the client's chart may have legal implications at some point in time. Thus, the written record of your time with the client and what you did with the client must be accurate.

Learning to effectively document the progress of a client takes time and practice. Be accurate while citing the correct time, date, and any other pertinent data. In being descriptive, focus on what actually occurred in the session, how things may have unfolded, and the nature of the music therapy intervention. Words need to be spelled correctly, as well as the correct word used to describe the event. I often use the analogy that the misspelled word is like the wrong note in a piece of music – it distracts the reader (listener), confuses the sentence (the musical phrase), and if there are enough of them, the thought that the writer is attempting to convey makes no sense at all. It is important for the grammar to be correct as it relates to the flow of the words and if it is not correct, misunderstanding and confusion take place. What good is it if you achieve a goal in a session and yet no one can understand that this has occurred because of the writing!

> These notes must be accurate,
> descriptive, free from spelling errors,
> and grammatically correct.

The notes in a client's chart are of utmost importance for all the aforementioned reasons; make sure that they are treated as such. Once in the chart they are part of a permanent record and cannot be altered.

DATA COLLECTION

Facilities/employers are interested in the data gathered on the client's behavior. Thus the data consists of behaviors that can be quantified and conveyed/recorded via documentation. I think it is very important to understand that there is a qualitative aspect to the music therapy process that as clinicians we are very much aware of. It is a given in the music therapy profession that the quality of life is enhanced through the music therapy experience. However, when it comes to an employing agency that must answer to a third party payer, or the employer concerned with hard results and data, as much as we believe in the spirit and art of what we do, it is still a business at some level to some person or entity. Thus, we are accountable for the effectiveness of our art and we need proficiency and accuracy in order to insure our accountability. Familiarity with the quantitative aspects of our profession is therefore a must.

In the treatment plan there is often a frequency, percentage, or other quantifiable method that is cited as an objective or goal for the client to achieve. This is also usually stated in terms of establishing, maintaining, reducing, or increasing a behavior. There are many different ways in which data can be gathered, but for our purposes, frequency, duration, and stimulus/response will be explained.

Frequency recording refers to the simple counting of a behavior during a specific time. Virtually any behavior can be counted using the frequency method. Here are some examples of this method:

- Hollye is an autistic child who makes little to no eye contact. The number of times in a session she looks into the eyes of the therapist is referred to as the frequency per session.
- Troy is an adolescent who shows poor impulse control in the area of verbal statements. The number of times he inappropriately interrupts others in a group may be counted as the frequency per session.
- Kiki is depressed woman who says little to no positive words or sentences. The number of positive statements said is the frequency per session.

Frequency recording is very easy to use and can be simply tallied. In actual clinical settings it may not be appropriate to tally every response during the session, but committing to memory events that are to be tallied is something that can be practiced and can become quite reliable. The data can also be represented in a percentage format. For example, with Troy we might be trying to decrease the percentage of inappropriate interrupting behavior.

Duration recording refers to the length of time that the behavior is occurring. Behavior occurs over time and when it is necessary to decrease the time of behavior rather than incidence, duration recording is utilized. Duration can be any segment of time such as seconds, minutes, hours, etc. In the case of Hollye that is mentioned in the frequency section, she may make eye contact several times during the session but the amount of time actually engaged in eye contact might be minimal. Instead of counting the number of times she engages in eye contact, we would be looking at increasing the length of time of time engaged in eye contact. This can also be represented as a percentage of time increased over a baseline.

> We are accountable for the effectiveness of our art, thus our notes must be accurate in order to insure our accountability.

There are times when the goal is based upon a relationship between a stimulus and response. For example, presenting a cue to Hollye: "Hollye, looked at me." Here we give an opportunity for a response and we note if the response is given. This can fall under frequency data collection and can be utilized to show a percentage of response. Along the same line, there may be a time factor involved where the response is to occur within a given time frame after a cue, to have the response last a certain amount of time after a cue, or a combination of both. In the above example it might be important to have Hollye respond within 3 seconds after the cue and/or to hold the contact for 2 seconds.

Descriptive Words and Phrases

In the writing of a progress note, many different types of words and phrases can be used to describe behavior. Often these words might be considered assessments of the client while at other times the actual description of the behavior is objective in nature. For example, to say that someone is happy is an assessment of the observation that he/she is smiling, laughing, has an appropriate rate of speech, and the content of his/her language is consistent in content with what a "happy" person might say. On the other hand, to say someone's smile looks tight, their eyes are fixed without blinking and their speech accelerated and bordering on incoherence is another thing. Yet, you initially notice that in both instances, you are starting with the observation that there is smile-like behavior. In writing the note about someone being happy you can state it in the following manner: *Tracy came into the session happy, as evidenced by her relaxed smile and pleasant conversation.*

The words listed below are often subjective in nature and with the addition of objective observations, a good picture of a person can be given.

EMOTIONAL STATUS

cheerful	confused	apathetic	hostile
enthusiastic	indifferent	sad	angry
bitter	despondent	nervous	agitated
excited	ambivalent	depressed	fearful
unemotional	withdrawn	gloomy	irritable
happy	labile	appropriate	detached
apathetic	anxious	worried	apprehensive

MOTOR BEHAVIOR

catatonic	hyperactive	energetic	slow
rigid	shuffling gait	tremor	slump posture
upward	lethargic	accelerated	agitated
hypersensitive	fidgety	sluggish	tenants
relaxed	muscle weakness		uncoordinated

COMMUNICATION

incoherence	verbose	rambling	dysarthic
talkative	quiet	word salad	argumentative
complaining	evasive	defensive	loud
boisterous	whispering	noisy	crying
screaming	shouting	whiner	ambiguous
communicative	vague	open	belligerent

incomplete sentences non-communicative
does not initiate conversation will only answer when spoken to
aspects of voice tone such as flat, normal, high pitch, low pitch.

PERSONALITY TRAITS

dependent	independent	overbearing	aggressive
hostile	compulsive	manipulative	destructive
capable	responsible	irresponsible	disrespectful
silly	cooperative	uncooperative	sincere
selfish	unselfish	tolerant	snobbish
sociable	unstable	temperamental	
superstitious	sympathetic	impulsive	shy
sophisticated	reserved	vindictive	thoughtful
tactless	ambitious	arrogant	affectionate
aloof	assertive	autocratic	boastful
bossy	calm	cautious	confident
careless	conceited	conscientious	
conservative	considerate	content	cruel
deceitful	defensive	inpatient	mischievous
pleasant	silent	self-centered	resentful
unaffected	sly	dignified	demanding
dependable	dominant	submissive	servile
masculine	effeminate	efficient	enthusiastic
evasive	humorous	high strung	idealistic
imaginative	immature	infantile	inhibited
intelligent	intolerant	mature	lazy
responsible	jolly	kind	outgoing
prejudiced	smug	rude	preoccupied
seclusive	friendly	seductive	

APPEARANCE

clean	neat	sloppy	unkempt
disheveled	uncombed	bizarrely dressed	overdressed
inappropriately dressed		appropriately dressed	
fussy	fastidious	looked tired	worn out

Methods of Documentation

When it comes to the actual process of documentation, there are a couple of methods that are generally utilized. The most common approaches are SOAP notes and narrative notes. Often the setting will dictate the manner in which the documentation is to be done and may, in fact, use a different set of guidelines than those that are given here.

The documentation of the session that is to be placed in the client's chart is normally called the "progress note." The progress note is a summary of the music therapy session in relationship to the movement towards the goal. Not everything that the client does is pertinent to the goals established, and therefore need not be cited in the progress note. If you're confused as to what to include, ask yourself these questions:

> "Is this related to my client's goal?"
> "If this event is not related to my client's goal, is it important enough for other treatment team members to know?"

When writing the progress note always write in the third person. If you are to refer to yourself do it as "this writer," "this music therapist," "this music therapy student," or "this music therapy intern."

> The progress note is a summary of the music therapy session in relationship to the progress towards the goal.

SOAP Notes

The first style is called the SOAP, which is an acronym for Subjective, Objective, Assessment and Plan.

S - Subjective: This is where to report data that is given to you by the client. It is often reported in quotation marks as something the client said. It is sometimes thought of as how the client is viewing the world. It might be what the client says regarding the activity, his/her feelings, concerns, or anything pertinent to his/her treatment.

O - Objective: This is where to record your objective unbiased observation of the client while he/she is in your session. This should be tied thematically to the Subjective section above. It is also helpful to briefly mention the musical environment (activity) from which these observations were taken.

A - Assessment: Up to this point, you have cited information that the client has given you, written an objective picture of the client related to this information, and briefly mentioned the musical intervention. The Assessment part of the note is how you will interpret these events from a subjective point of view. You should relate this interpretation to the goals and objectives that you have been addressing through the music therapy treatment as well as to the (S) and (O) sections previously written. This section is your professional opinion, and must be treated very carefully as you want to stay within the bounds of your knowledge and expertise.

P - Plan: This part reflects your future treatment strategy, interventions, or actions related to the client's achievement of his/her goal. It may consist of recommendations regarding the treatment plant and goals of the client.

Narrative Notes

The narrative note does not have an acronym as a SOAP note does. It is a basic objective view of the client in the session in relation to the goals and objectives set forth with little assessment given. It is written in a paragraph format. It focuses on the actual events of the session regarding what the client did in relationship to the music therapy intervention. The type of music therapy intervention should be briefly identified. The end of the note should include a plan of action for future sessions to help continuity of documentation.

Examples of Progress Notes

The progress notes given below describe hypothetical individuals. A SOAP note will be followed by narrative note based on the same session. After the two notes are given, they will be presented again with comments inserted that explain various aspects of the note. These comments will be separated via parentheses and italics from the actual note.

The first note is about a 15-year-old male who is currently hospitalized for a suicide attempt.

> **S:** "They haven't let me have my guitar for three weeks."
> "This was cool... I will work on it more."
> **O:** Client was holding the guitar close to his chest, hugging it to him. As he made this statement his voice was calm and at a low volume. Client then proceeded to participate in creative songwriting activity. The client's lyrics reflected emotional themes centered on a relationship with an old girlfriend. At the end of the session, the client verbalized appreciation to the music therapist for helping him with the songwriting process.
> **A:** Initially, the client showed a great deal of positive emotion towards holding his guitar. The instrument seems important to the client as a means of emotional outlet. The client again, as in previous sessions, focused on a past relationship where he spoke of

being sad regarding the loss of an important relationship. The words that the client put to music expressed appropriately the sadness that the client felt. At the end of the session there was a visible change in affect, as the client appeared more relaxed with a positive mood as evidenced by smiling. He also verbalized that he was going to work on the song more.

P: Continue with half-hour individual music therapy sessions focusing on emotional outlet through creative songwriting. Attempt to expand range of topics from the loss of a girlfriend to family relationships, and internal struggles.

Narrative Note

In an individual music therapy songwriting session the client emotionally expressed appreciation for being able to play his guitar that he had not been able to access for the past three weeks. The client composed a song consisting of feelings of loss regarding a relationship with a girl that had been terminated by the girl. The song seemed to accurately reflect the client's feelings of sadness. At the end of the session the client appeared more relaxed as evidenced by smiling and expressed appreciation to the music therapist for helping him write the song. In future sessions the client will be encouraged to explore more themes such as family relationships and internal struggles. The plan is to continue seeing the client twice a week for half-hour individual music therapy sessions.

The two notes are now analyzed and compared for content.

S: "They haven't let me have my guitar for three weeks." "This was cool... I will work on it more." *(Here are two comments. One is from the beginning and one is from the end of the session. These comments are important as they refer to emotional states. Utilizing a phrase from the song may also have been appropriate here.)*

O: Client was holding the guitar close to his chest, hugging it to him. *(Here is a physical picture of the client that illustrates a feeling. Note,* *however, that the feeling is not mentioned or interpreted at this point.)* As he made this statement his voice was calm and at a low volume. *(This is also an objective observation that is simply mentioned. It does, however, provide for a basis of interpretation later.)* Client then proceeded to participate in creative songwriting activity. *(Here the content of the type of music therapy intervention is made.)* The client's lyrics reflected emotional themes centered on a relationship with an old girlfriend. At the end of the session, the client verbalized appreciation to the music therapist for helping him with the songwriting process. *(This section concludes by first mentioning that the words of the song were emotional in nature, and near the end of the session the client said something to the therapist that showed appreciation.)*

A: Initially, the client showed a great deal of positive emotion towards holding his guitar. The instrument seems important to the client as a means of emotional outlet. *(The first comment in the (S) is addressed and the first observation is addressed. The mentioning of "positive emotion" is the assessment of the statement combined with the objective observation. Note the use of the word "seems" in the second sentence. The utilization of this word suggests that it is not a given fact, but rather the interpretation of the writer.)* The client again, as in previous sessions, *(the connection of treatment sessions)* focused on a past relationship where he spoke of being sad regarding the loss of an important relationship. The words that the client put to music expressed appropriately the sadness that the client felt. *(The writer is stating that there was congruence in the emotional expression. If the client had written something inappropriate, it would be addressed here and noted as such.)* At the end of the session there was a visible change in affect, as the client appeared more relaxed with a positive mood as evidenced by smiling. He verbalized that he was going to work on the song more. *(This ties into the second quote in the (S) section as well as the end of the (O) section. Note the use of 'as evidenced by' so that the assessment in grounded in an objective observation.)*

P: Continue with half-hour individual music therapy sessions focusing on emotional outlet through creative songwriting. Attempt to expand range of topics from the loss of a girlfriend to family relationships, and internal struggles. *(The plan is discussed for the future. Frequency is mentioned as well as the direction of treatment. This leaves the door open for the next progress note where new themes may be explored and developed.)*

Now examine the narrative note.

In a 1:1 music therapy songwriting session the client emotionally expressed appreciation for being able to play his guitar that he had not been able to access for the past three weeks. *(A basic opening statement that states that this was an individual music therapy session that focused on an activity – songwriting, and that the client was appreciative of getting his guitar.)* The client composed a song consisting of feelings of loss regarding a relationship with a girl that had been terminated by the girl. *(A basic objective statement of what the client did – notice that there is no assessment at this point.)* The song seemed to accurately reflect the client's feelings of sadness. *(Here the use of the word "seemed" is non-committal but reflective of what the writer sensed. It is a very mild assessment, at best, of the content of the song.)* At the end of the session the client appeared more relaxed as evidenced by smiling and expressed appreciation to the music therapist for helping him write the song. *(The end of the session is noted, as there seems to be a change of overall feeling of the client. Note the use of "as evidenced by" so that the assessment in grounded in an objective observation.)* In future sessions the client will be encouraged to explore more themes such as family relationships, and internal struggles. The plan is to continue seeing the client twice a week for half-hour individual music therapy sessions. *(The note ends with a look to the future and the frequency of treatment.)*

Termination Note

There comes a time in treatment when termination is warranted. The discontinuation of music therapy treatment may occur for a variety of reasons such as: the client reaching the goals stated in the treatment plan; a decision made that the client will no longer benefit from music therapy; a scheduling conflict occurs that prevents the client from attending sessions; or the client being discharged from the treatment facility. When this time comes, a termination note is needed to complete the file. This note will summarize the progress of the client throughout the music therapy treatment. Additionally it may address other areas of future goals and interventions. If you are working on a treatment team this final note may be written as a group if that is the policy of the institution.

SOME GENERAL GUIDELINES

Below is a list of some general guidelines that share common ground throughout many types of facilities and populations.

- All notes should indicate the date, the fact that this is a music therapy note, and be signed at the end and initialed with the appropriate professional designation.

Example: June 30, 2003 - Music Therapy (then the note follows). At the end of the note sign your name and cite your credential. Here are some common designations used un the music therapy profession: MT (Music Therapist); MT-BC (Music Therapist Board Certified); MTS (music Therapy Student); MTI (music Therapy Intern).

- Notes should reflect the client's functional abilities.
- Report any progress by the client and back up with objective data.
- Cite pathological interference with appropriate functioning.
- Be sure to be citing relationship of treatment to the client's treatment plan and give raw data if appropriate.
- Mention the music therapy intervention, but do not feel the need to go into detail as to the aspects of it.

- Keep the note about the client. Focus on his/her involvement. Do not go off into tangents.
- Indicate the follow up plans and continuity of treatment. It is OK to look at where the client has been and what is planned for the future.
- Notes should be clear in language with statements that are direct illustrations of what has occurred. With this in mind be concise and to the point.
- Make sure your spelling and grammar are correct.
- Use professional language; do not use slang.
- If a client is not attending the music therapy session, the note should reflect any attempts to locate the client or knowledge of his/her whereabouts.
- If you make an error, draw a line through it, initial it and note the date and time.

SUMMARY

This chapter looks at the important process of documentation in the work setting. In most facilities there is a process of documentation that follows the client. Most commonly a client is:

- Admitted
- Assessed by various disciplines
- A treatment plan is developed from the assessments
- Goals are drawn from the treatment plan
- A referral is made to music therapy
- The client is then assessed by a music therapist
- Objectives are drawn up from the goals given
- A music therapy strategy is developed and implemented
- Progress notes are written and placed in the chart. At some point the client may be terminated from music therapy and at that time, a "termination note" is written.

If you are involved in a private practice, however, a referral is received for music therapy and then you do an assessment. As there is no formal treatment team, you are the primary decision maker as to what goals are to be addressed based on all the information you have gathered.

Learning how to write concise and clear objectives is critical to the planning of effective music therapy treatment strategies. The session, while planned out, must be fluid and address the changing moments of the music therapy session. Being cognizant of the client's needs in the moment while keeping an eye on the goal is a learned skill that must be developed.

SOAP and narrative notes are two formats that are commonly seen in various settings. These progress notes must be accurate in all aspects of language, grammar, and most importantly, content. They become part of a written record that is permanent and may have implications beyond the treatment of the client.

Documentation is often the area that is looked at most closely by administrators and those involved in quality assurance. Accurate documentation can make or break the validity of music therapy, and thus cannot be taken lightly.

Chapter 7

BEGINNING TO BUILD YOUR STYLE

Style is a general pattern of behaviors, thoughts, strategies, techniques and philosophy upon which you center your basic music therapy approach. It eventually becomes an integral part of you as a person as well as a music therapist. It defines you in your work with your clients and is often fluid in character as clients present different obstacles in treatment.

READ AND UNDERSTAND THEORY

In building your style, knowledge of psychological theory, music therapy theory and counseling theory is imperative. Without a basic understanding of knowing how people develop, why they do the things they do, and what techniques you can utilize to help them progress towards their goals, you have no real starting point.

You will find as you work with clients of various populations and disabilities, your treatment approaches might change. You may, however, begin to resonate with a certain philosophical approach. If this occurs, search beyond that which is given in class. As you attend conferences, go to sessions that seem to be linked with this particular philosophical approach. Research the various techniques that are utilized in the approach and internalize them as part of your style. Additionally, if you can get on the mailing lists for social workers, counselors, or psychologists, you can possibly attend workshops where the philosophy and techniques are explored through these types of professionals. This is a most valuable way to advance your knowledge in a given direction. I feel that often these workshops are extremely helpful in understanding the practical application of theory; afterwards, use your creativity to transfer the knowledge to your music therapy practice. Often an added bonus to attending non-music therapy workshops is the possibility of making valuable contacts for later in your career.

> Go beyond what is given in class. Stretch
> yourself and investigate the modality to
> which you are drawn.

Additionally, review your music therapy theory. Go back through class lectures and workshops to refresh your memory throughout your development. Make it a goal to read new texts and journals. The field is constantly developing and to be "current in the field" is an asset that can often distinguish you from others.

FIND A MENTOR

One of the most valuable tools in developing your style is finding a mentor or someone you can use as a role model. A mentor is someone who is mature in knowledge and experience and is willing to selflessly share these things with you. Mentors can be hard to find, but are priceless to your development of style. Once a mentor is found, he/she should be cherished and used wisely. A good way to learn from a mentor is to spend time watching him/her work. In watching him/her work, notice:

- How and what words are used - instructions, feedback, acknowledgement, reinforcement, and processing skills.
- How music is used and when - is it recorded, live, what styles are being utilized.
- When there is silence, what is the purpose of the silence.
- His/her musical skills - what particular skills can you emulate.
- Mannerisms - body language.
- The interaction (therapy) with the client(s) – notice theory that is now put into practice.
- Involvement in professional associations.

A good mentor will appreciate questions. Often the questions will also put the mentor into a re-evaluative mode regarding the session that can also be helpful to the mentor. Develop a relationship with and be thankful for the mentor. If appropriate, you might want to do something nice for him/her that shows your appreciation.

OBSERVE

Vicarious learning is being able to learn from others through observation. Observing other music therapists is a wonderful way to see theory in action. Being able to spend time with the music therapist after the session and being afforded time to discuss aspects of the session is a great bonus. By observing different therapists you can begin to understand the many aspects of personal style that fit within various theoretical parameters. Observing two different music therapists with a behavioral approach with a given population can be an enlightening experience. How they use positive reinforcement and their scheduling of it may differ, yet be equally effective. In the same manner, watching two therapists who are more humanistic and perhaps are more inclined towards the approach of Carl Rogers will be similarly enlightening. Understanding how the music therapist is utilizing music in the session can help in giving you ideas for your own work. Music skills combined with his/her personal style can be a model for you as you grow.

Apart from just watching the therapist in action, you can learn a great deal by watching how the client is moving through the music therapy session. Noticing the interaction between the client and therapist is always important, but also take note of how the client interacts with the music. Notice what the client does if he/she is disengaged from the therapist and/or the music. If it is an improvisational session, notice what instrument(s) the client is using and how the client is playing the instrument(s) as well as they way the client physically holds and interacts with the instrument(s). Listen to the inflection of the sounds the client is creating. Do the sounds have rhythm? Are they organized in a rhythmic motif? Are the sounds in response to the therapist, something in the environment, or creatively initiated? Is there form to the playing? Is there a tonal center, and if so is there inherent tension and resolution?

Through this type of observation you begin to understand where the client is both musically and developmentally. You can learn what "works" with them and what may not be effective. The observation of the musical client is critical.

With this in mind, watching how the client interacts with music is almost like learning a different language. Keep in mind that each client is inherently musical, and because of this human quality he/she is constantly making music. As a musician you can hear (or see in the body language) the characteristics of music (form, melody, timbre, rhythm, harmony, and texture). As a therapist you begin to understand what the client is trying to tell you through this language. By understanding this language, you can have a more meaningful interaction with the client through a music therapy session.

> Clients are inherently musical and as a
> music therapist you can hear (or see in
> the body language) the
> elements of music.

EXPERIENCE

The old adage that "nothing replaces experience" is partially true. To move into an experience with a knowledge base that prepares you at least minimally for what is about to happen can enhance your learning through the experience. So, in reality, nothing replaces experience except experience plus preparation.

If you have done the theoretical preparation, the observations, and you are comfortable with who you are, moving into experience is the next step in defining your style. As you move through initial music therapy experiences, you can begin to assess your own comfort level with various interventions and techniques. You will begin to learn what works best for your client(s) and what behaviors and interventions you need to perform to help the client(s) progress towards their goals.

In developing style, you are involved in utilizing the technique of music therapy. This technique is much like employing technique on any musical instrument. On a musical instrument you try new behaviors to help develop skills, then repeat and refine these behaviors (practice) in an attempt to proficiently perform the repertoire you are learning. In music therapy, the skills that you refine in class lab situations and in practicum help in your development of style.

Your presence in the session can take many forms and it will shift with the flow of the session. This fluidity of style comes through experience and your repertoire of skills will gradually increase as you conduct more and more sessions. Eventually, your technique will develop to a level where you will be comfortable with many different types of populations, settings, and music therapy interventions.

REFLECT

To reflect means to review all that has occurred and then evaluate. This often begins as soon as the session ends by writing in a journal. Some things that you should address in the journal are:

- Your immediate feelings about the session.
- What interventions seemed to work.
- What interventions did not seem to work.
- Behaviors that the client engaged in that stand out in your memory.
- Things that you think you did well.
- Things that you think should be changed.
- What was the overall quality of the music used by you.

Videotaping your sessions is the best way to learn from reflection. Videotape (like the microphone when you tape your musical practice sessions or performances) doesn't lie. It is a tool that will help you to learn about your style and your client. You can observe your reactions and interactions as well as the client's within the session. You can learn (as it applies to you as well as to your client) about body language, reinforcement, acceptance, critical interventions, listening, musical reactions, and musical interactions. Reviewing the videotape with a supervisor is most helpful. The supervisor can help you identify and learn about cause and effect relationships.

SUMMARY

Much of this handbook ultimately relates to the question of style. In looking at who you are, your musicianship, your philosophical orientation, and your personal attributes, your style begins to take shape. Being a person who wants to help others is at the core of your style. Through being a musician and artist, the style develops. The combination of music, art, and altruism makes one a unique person, and style is set in motion.

To gain knowledge about personality development is to gain insight in the reasons why people do the things they do. To define and argue about what is "normal" is part of an educational process that helps in your cognitive understanding of this dilemma. Knowledge of diagnostic criteria that separate one behavior disorder from another is necessary and valuable. Working with those who are classified by a diagnosis demands an understanding of various intervention strategies. These strategies are grounded in theories often so philosophically distant from one another it is hard to say that there is only one way to help people achieve their goals. The relationship of these philosophies and approaches to music therapy is in the process of constant growth. The leaders in the field of music therapy utilize aspects of different theories with equal effectiveness. Finding the right orientation for the population you work with is a major aspect of style development. It is important to be knowledgeable and comfortable with the techniques and strategies of the chosen philosophical approach.

To meet someone who has effectively adapted music therapy technique into a style that you admire is a wonderful asset to your growth. To find a mentor and identify him/her as such can enter you into a valuable and often endearing relationship. This relationship is one not to be taken for granted, but to be cherished for the learning that can result from it. Your mentor can help you in your definition of style, be a model for you, and guide you into your professional life.

Observation as a tool for growth, is basically broken down into five areas: 1) observing the therapist, 2) observing the client, 3) observing the interaction between the therapist and client, 4) observing the interaction of the client with the music, and 5) observing the use of music "as" or "in" therapy as employed by the music therapist. The events and behaviors you will see are many: body language, verbalizations, vocalizations, music and silence are just some areas of focus. Note how they all interact to produce the flow of the session; even if the session seems scattered and not cohesive, it is all part of the flow.

To have knowledge-based experiences is truly the beginning of understanding your style. Once you are in a session and moving through it, you are starting to really develop your sense of music therapy. Utilizing music therapy with a wide variety of populations helps you to understand how your style will transform and transfer from one client group to the next. While being a very "accepting" music therapist, you may learn that with certain clientele, a strong set of limits might need to be in place in order for the session to progress in a therapeutic fashion. In other situations you may find that your role is primarily one of a facilitator and the process unfolds before you. Growth via experience is paramount in importance when looking at establishing your style.

Reflecting on your experiences is essential to understand the development of style. Why you used a specific music intervention at a particular time, for this particular client, and the success of the session, can be explored. Your responses and reactions as well as the client's responses and reactions are reviewed to see the interrelationships between you and client, the client and the music, and you and the music. Using videotape is the best way to accurately review these responses. The videotape allows you to see these relationships develop during the session. Through this review, you can see aspects of your style that need to be addressed as well as aspects that seem comfortable and effective.

In music, the Classical Style and Baroque Style are both aspects of music with different methods of composition and form, yet both are pleasing. The broader picture of music encompasses them both, and music in both styles is effectively expressive. In speaking about the style of being a music therapist, there are different approaches based on numerous factors. In your development of style, you will see that, ultimately, who you are as a person, your life, your experience and the nature of your clients have a part in defining your unique style.

Chapter 8

GETTING THE MOST FROM SUPERVISION

By Holly Baxter, MT-BC

Supervision has been a major influence in each of our lives in one form or another. Whether from a family member, manager or professor, supervision provides information about who we are, how we operate and how we can improve upon what we do. The information in this chapter can strongly influence the success of your supervisory relationship and, ultimately, your educational and professional career.

THE NECESSITY OF SUPERVISION

Clinical supervision as defined by Loganbill, Hardy & Delworth (1982) is "an intensive, interpersonally focused, one-to-one relationship in which one person is designated to facilitate the development of therapeutic competence in the other person." Most important in this definition is the key idea of "facilitation". Supervisors, like music therapists, cannot, in and of themselves, create change. Supervisors can only provide the environment and the feedback which encourage growth and learning. It is up to the supervisee to act upon the knowledge and experience given to them.

Supervision is one of the fundamental methods through which students acquire the skills necessary to practice music therapy competently and ethically (Dileo, 2001) and includes teaching, modeling, observing, shaping, coaching and evaluation of skills and behaviors (McClain, 2001). Without supervision, there is no external point of reference and often little impetus to learn new techniques or skills. A skilled supervisor challenges students and therapists to challenge themselves and provides a wealth of firsthand experience.

Additionally, having another's input as to style, repertoire, clinical choices and techniques can be invaluable in meeting the needs of a client. Although accepting criticism may be difficult, a student who strives to learn from supervision by remaining open and taking an active role has much to gain.

> Supervision helps us understand how to improve upon what we do.

In music therapy work you will find that each client you work with has a unique set of strengths and challenges. Throughout your academic and professional career you will need to adapt continuously to meet each client as an individual. Without the oversight and input of supervisors, it is virtually impossible to do this demanding work. Developing and maintaining strong supervisory relationships is key to your success.

THE SUPERVISORY RELATIONSHIP

Forinash (2001) states that, "Supervision is a relationship, one in which both supervisor and supervisee actively participate and interact – not simply following a recipe, but engaging in a rich and dynamic relationship." The "dynamic relationship" can start with you taking an active role in your practical learning. Consider the following:

- An initial meeting prior to beginning fieldwork. The student may wish to request this if it is not included in the usual process, and it may be conducted in person or by telephone.
- Attendance at a lecture or training facilitated by the supervisor. The student should inquire as to these opportunities during the initial meeting.
- Conference attendance during which the student can seek out the potential supervisor.

During these initial meetings the following techniques can further establish a relationship with your supervisor:

- If in a group situation, be sure to introduce yourself and explain your purpose for being there.
- Be attentive to any information given by the supervisor and ask pertinent questions.
- Offer information about yourself that pertains to the situation.
- If the opportunity presents itself, feel free to just talk (Borczon, 1997) about the day, the event or yourself.
- Be sure to present yourself as you would like to be seen. Appropriate attire, language and preparation are important to a strong first impression. Remain attentive and use body language that communicates attentiveness.

Situation: John is attending a lecture given by the music therapist who will be his next fieldwork supervisor. During the break, John approaches the podium and introduces himself.

> *John:* Hello, my name is John Smith and I hope to be working with you this year.
> *Supervisor:* It's nice to meet you.
> *John:* I'm enjoying your discussion very much, but I was wondering, when you spoke of assigning various instruments to the archetypes in your story, I wasn't sure how you made those decisions.
> *Supervisor:* Good point, I'll be covering this more after the break.
> *John:* Great. I'm very interested in the archetypal idea myself. I've read much of Carl Jung's work and look forward to knowing more about combining it with music.

This conversation allows John to explore his supervisor's openness to questions, knowledge of the subject and relationship with students. In addition, it identifies John to the supervisor as someone who takes his learning seriously. Later, near the water cooler, John begins another conversation:

John: I'm extremely excited to begin at your site. It will be a new population for me, but one that I've always been interested in.

Supervisor: It certainly has kept me interested. I think you'll enjoy your time at our facility.

This begins a second conversation that is more familiar and allows the Supervisor to know more personal information about John, insuring the Supervisor will remember John.

Common Ground

With such a tremendous variety of music therapy interventions, client populations and musical styles, it is exciting to think of all there is to learn from others. However, it is also important to have some common ground on which you and your supervisor can meet upon before moving forward. Common ground with your supervisor may include a shared respect for a particular model of music therapy work or philosophy, a common musical instrument, or even an appreciation for a certain musical style. It is not necessary that you and your supervisor have perfectly matching styles and interests and, in fact, it may be difficult for a beginning music therapist to define their own style or philosophy early in their career. However, the idea of common ground should be considered when beginning any supervisory relationship and can be explored in the following ways:

- Attend seminars or lectures given by your proposed supervisor. These will generally be focused in an area of expertise or special interest of the supervisor.
- Observe the supervisor in their work. Many music therapists work in settings in which observation is possible.
- Meet with your potential supervisor. Questions which could be asked during this time include:
- What degrees or credentials do you hold and where did you get them?
- Do you have a particular focus of client population in your work? How did you arrive at choosing this focus?

- Do you have a particular methodology that you prefer to use? Where did you learn this methodology and why is it especially effective?
- Search the Journal of Music Therapy, Music Therapy Perspectives or music therapy texts for articles written by your proposed supervisor to assess their area of expertise.

In finding a supervisor who has similar interests or philosophies, a rapport can develop based in these areas. As the relationship develops, the common ground that has been established will allow you to relate with the supervisor on many different levels.

Uncommon Ground

It is possible that you may have the opportunity to work in a fieldwork setting in which there is not a music therapist on staff. Your work would then be supervised by a professional in another field in conjunction with your university faculty. In such cases you may find yourself asking the following questions:

Question: What can I learn from a professional in this field?
Answer: Professionals in other fields provide information and support of a technical nature that may be out of the normal range of knowledge for a music therapist. The receptive student will find much to learn from a professional who has studied another aspect of client functioning or mode of therapeutic work.
Question: Does this professional have a supportive view of music therapy and the knowledge necessary to provide feedback?
Answer: Your initial meeting will provide information as to the professional's view of music therapy. Questions to ask of the professional include: Have you worked with music therapy students previously? Why do you wish to integrate music therapy into your facility? How do you think your clients may benefit from music therapy?
Question: What forum will I have to discuss practical issues regarding my music therapy work (i.e. musical skills, instrumentation, song choices)?

Answer: All field study or practicum assignments are also discussed within the educational setting. Ideally, a designated class or meeting time takes place weekly to discuss music therapy skills as well as other growth and learning issues that may arise.

Supervision Style

Each practicum site or internship has its own personality and style. Some emphasize experiential learning and others can be more oriented towards observation and discussion. Some present a casual and relaxed atmosphere while many are more traditional in approach. Accordingly each facility has its own manner of conducting supervision. Whatever this view may be, you should be aware of the practical aspects of your supervisor's style and how to utilize it for learning. Asking yourself the following questions may provide insight into your own needs for supervision and how they mesh with your supervisor's style:

Question: Do I work better one-on-one or in a peer group environment?
To answer this, examine your past educational experiences and determine which environment has been most comfortable and beneficial to your growth. You may also wish to examine your own ideas of whether peer group support is beneficial to growth.
Question: Do I require a relationship with a specific supervisor or am I more comfortable working with a supervisory team?
For this, reflect on past experience and whether you tend to return consistently to a single mentor or gather information from a variety of persons when making decisions. Examine what your image of an ideal supervisor is and ask yourself whether a single person can meet that ideal.
Question: Do I work best with constant daily feedback or more intermittent critique, i.e. weekly or monthly?
Ask yourself if you speak with friends every day to discuss daily events or if you only reach out to others during important decision making times.

The answers to each of these questions provide information regarding the supervisory relationship that may work best for you. If you find that your preferred supervisory style differs from that of your supervisor, discussing these differences together will open the door towards learning.

MODE OF SUPERVISION – LIVE VERSUS VIDEO

Your fieldwork and internship programs will often utilize a variety of means for supervision. Generally, both live and recorded observation methods are used for a well-rounded supervisory process.

The videotaping of a clinical session provides a simple means through which to review material with your supervisor. The accessibility of videotape allows for techniques and activities to be discussed thoroughly as to efficacy, appropriateness and client response. Through reviewing the videotaped sessions over a period of time, skills that have been developed or need further improvement are clearly seen and allows for objective discussion of the session between you and your supervisor. In addition, beginning therapists may find it very difficult to recall information from the session in order to properly assess and document meetings with a client. Videotape can provide this recall in order that the therapist may focus on attending to the client's needs during a session rather than mentally cataloging activities and responses.

A supervisor who is present at a music therapy session is able to provide a different and necessary viewpoint. Affect, mood and pacing are just a few of the elements which are most easily evaluated while the session is taking place and do not transfer well to videotape. In addition, early sessions can be quite overwhelming for a newer therapist or student, especially if things do not go as planned. Reviewing such a session immediately afterwards can be difficult or even emotional, but is often necessary in order to process reactions and interactions thoroughly.

Both live and videotaped supervision have unique benefits, and should be utilized for a total supervisory experience.

Making Feedback Work For You

It can be very difficult to open oneself up to viewpoints regarding what is working and what is not. This is the point when the supervisor's style and the student's learning style must mesh in order that critique can be presented in a useful manner and received with some degree of objectivity. A strong rapport with your supervisor will benefit you greatly during critique. This mutual understanding and trust will facilitate the openness and honesty which is important in making feedback work for you. Treating all aspects of your work with utmost professionalism and sincerity can encourage strong rapport as well as a openness to new ideas and a positive attitude towards learning, beginning with your initial meeting and continuing on through all of your dealings with your supervisor.

In addition to a strong rapport and understanding learning styles, the actual meeting in which critique is presented is a time for being proactive and present. There are two main concepts to remember when making feedback work for you. The first is insuring your willingness to learn and the second is filtering information appropriately.

Willingness to Learn

Farnan's (1998) criteria for willingness to learn include being receptive to feedback, asking pertinent questions and asking for additional readings or resources.

BEING RECEPTIVE TO FEEDBACK   When working with a supervisor, it is important to "listen for understanding rather than for agreement" (Bright, 1988). Too many times we listen not as a learner but rather as a judge, weighing each aspect of what is said as to whether we agree or disagree. At this point, the student's primary task is to depersonalize criticism and view it as information worthy of objective examination (Bright, 1988). The following techniques may assist you in remaining receptive to feedback:

- Checking in with yourself mentally during supervisory meetings to assess your emotional or physical responses.
- Taking notes during supervisory meetings to defray the need to immediately respond to the feedback as well as to provide information for later review.
- Scheduling supervisory meetings during a low-stress time, i.e., avoid scheduling after long classes, work hours or directly after difficult sessions.
- Reviewing your personal goals before the meeting in order to provide perspective and the ability to see a broader view.

ASKING PERTINENT QUESTIONS Taking an active role in supervision requires that you ask questions during the supervisory process. These questions may be specifically about the session at hand or encompass a broader sense of your work. Such questions may be:
How often do you suggest that I offer positive reinforcement to this client?

- What types of strumming patterns do you think would work with this song?
- Have you noticed any specific areas of growth for the client during my work with him?
- What elements of my leadership should I work on?
- Is a behavioral approach the best mode for this client?
- Is my pacing effective during the session?
- Am I moving between activities too quickly or not quickly enough?
- How do you suggest I develop my activities further?
- What might I do to redirect the client's inappropriate behavior?

ASKING FOR ADDITIONAL READINGS OR RESOURCES With a heavy class schedule as well as fieldwork, you may feel that it is impossible to add additional learning to your caseload. However, utilizing readings or resources outside the standard curriculum not only presents a willingness to learn, but actually creates an environment in which learning happens more rapidly and with greater integration. A single idea presented by a single textbook can be easily forgotten. When that idea is read in another context, seen in action and discussed with peer groups, it becomes knowledge.

Filtering Information

In filtering information it is helpful to categorize the information as it comes in. During supervisory meetings, taking notes that divide information into musical, clinical, administrative or work habits can help you to expend appropriate energy and clearly focus on what is needed. In addition, this serves as a record of your growth.

The most important aspect of filtering information is consciously accepting the need to take action. If you don't make this decision in a conscious manner, you may lack the dedication necessary to make changes. Taking a step-by-step approach to making this determination (Bright, 1988) can provide the necessary structure to qualify critique as it is presented.

1. Assess the qualifications of the giver/supervisor. In some situations, such a group supervision or classroom discussions, you may receive critique from someone other than a designated supervisor. In such cases, you may find yourself evaluating whether or not the giver of the critique is qualified to provide the feedback. However, remaining receptive to new information is imperative to the learning process. Other professionals and peers have much to offer in the way of objective information, feedback and constructive critique.

2. Assess the bounds of the relationship with the giver/supervisor. Critique can be offered in many ways and on many levels. A professional setting and relationship are the most advantageous means through which to conduct the supervisory relationship. Such a setting and relationship focus on the learning of the student as well as the needs of the client. With this in mind it is helpful to conduct supervisory meetings in a pre-specified place at an agreed upon time. Try to avoid presenting issues or questions regarding your work outside of this setting. In addition, treat supervisory meetings as you would your sessions, including appropriate attire, manner, materials and confidentiality.

In rare instances, you may find yourself questioning the boundaries of the supervisory relationship. It is important in clinical supervision to keep in mind that many aspects of a therapist's personal life directly affect client progress. A supervisor who comments on inappropriate attire, affect, language or personal issues interfering with clinical work is very clearly operating within the bounds of the supervisory relationship. With this in mind, supervision can be a time of professional as well as personal growth (Feiner, 2001). Remaining receptive to supervisory information is key to such evolvement.

3. Assess the intention of the giver/supervisor. Ideally, a critique is presented with the full intention of bettering the student and thereby helping the client. However, unless this is the belief of the student, constructive feedback might be disregarded. The following questions may help the student to assess intent:

- Could you explain your critique in another way?
- Is this the first time you have noticed this about my work?
- Do you or have you had any other students having difficulty in this area?
- Have you ever had an experience similar to this?
- What do you suggest I do to fix the problem?

4. Assess your understanding. In taking an active role in supervision, it is essential that you ask the appropriate questions and collect the necessary information in order to completely understand the critique being given. However, your objective at this point is that of seeking information, rather than challenging critique. Seeking information puts the focus on you as the student and what you can do to better your work. Challenging critique operates in a defensive manner by minimizing the critique of the supervisor and creating a situation in which the supervisor must defend his or her position. Outlined below are some appropriate ways to seek information from your supervisor:

- Seeking Information: What part of the session should I be focusing on?
- Challenging Critique: What part of my session do you *think* is wrong?

Stating that the supervisor only *"thinks"* rather than knows challenges the supervisor's knowledge and authority. Asking what is "wrong" is changing the focus from bettering your work to fixing something that is broken.

- Seeking Information: How could I do the activity more effectively?
- Challenging Critique: Why isn't what I did okay?

Asking in this manner intimates that you believe it was okay and the supervisor must then provide information to the contrary.

- Seeking Information: Could you give me more specifics?
- Challenging Critique: What exactly are you talking about?

Asking the supervisor to clarify in this challenging tone shifts the focus from the student's work and to the supervisor's critique.

5. Assess your feelings. Accepting supervision can be very difficult and, at times, emotional. Taking written notes during supervisory meetings can prevent this emotional process from impeding on the assimilation of important information. Working through the feelings associated with the supervisory process at a later date is important to your professional and personal growth. This can be done through a variety of means – journaling, peer group support, therapy – however, it should be done in a proactive manner in order to prevent emotions from blocking positive growth. In addition, you may wish to explore emotional issues associated with supervision to gain a deeper understanding of your own needs and strengths. A strong emotional response may warrant a discussion with your supervisor or a qualified therapist.

SELF-CRITIQUE AND EVALUATION

Although not technically considered supervision, self-critique and evaluation both play an important role in the growth of any student. According to Bright (1988), "All the power of criticism is present in self-criticism. With control, it can become a way to energize ourselves for greater accomplishments – it can lead to the strongest kind of empowerment." Alley (1980) found that self-analysis of videotapes according to predetermined definitions and criteria seemed to substantially increase skills in a music therapy setting. As stated above, however, without formal supervision as well, there is very little means with which to gauge the objectivity of such critique.

When conducting self-critique, it is necessary to be objective. A biased critique can cause more damage than good. To avoid a biased self-critique, prepare your self-evaluations as if they were for another person. Take the same consideration with detail and, most importantly, be sure to balance praise and critique. You may also wish to receive your self-critique as if it were coming from someone else. Just as you would in a supervisory session, review all materials with a paper and pen to take note of exactly what is happening in the session. Written feedback provides structure that may take the ambiguity out of supervision (Farnan, 1996) and also provides an objective list of strengths and weaknesses rather than a mental catalogue that may veer more towards one than the other. This also allows for later review to determine growth and success over the long term.

It is also advisable to wait a sufficient amount of time after the session to review videotape or recordings. In clinical training the responsibility for the therapeutic situation can add an element of stress and anxiety which makes it difficult to even recall details of a session. Reviewing a clinical situation at a later time can allow you to be more objective.

Lastly, be sure to have the goals and objectives for the client at hand during the review process. As the basis for your work with the client, it provides a context for events that occur during the session.

WORKING THROUGH PROBLEM AREAS

Even with all of the essential elements in place, there are times when a supervisory relationship may be difficult. Personality conflicts, questions of judgment or disagreements regarding technique can all set the stage for an unproductive educational setting. However, part of taking an active role in supervision is understanding that all relationships present an opportunity for growth and require work and endurance in order to succeed. "Splitting" of supervisors, i.e. creating division between supervisors by unjustly criticizing or undermining one or the other, is in all cases inappropriate and detrimental to all parties. Splitting may take the form of criticizing a field work supervisor during class time with a professor, discussing disagreements with your supervisor's superior in an informal manner, or questioning the abilities of a professor in the presence of your field work supervisor.

> When in a problematic relationship, remember it is also an opportunity for growth.

Although it may be tempting to air grievances publicly, it is important to approach problematic circumstances in a professional and thoughtful manner. The American Music Therapy Association Code of Ethics model can be adapted to working through difficult supervisory issues in the following ways:

- The student should consult first with the supervisor and discuss possible actions. It is also suggested that the student and supervisor document this consultation. Circumstances which warrant this step may include insufficient time provided to the student for supervisory meetings, inappropriate or "out of bounds" feedback or a general feeling of apprehension or fear from the student during meetings. A difference of opinion on specific issues in training or lack of support for a particular

> mode of working should also be discussed in this forum but would not usually warrant moving on to the next step.
> * If the difficulty is not resolved through this consultation, and the circumstance is extreme, i.e. jeopardizing the student's education or client safety, the student may bring the situation to the attention of the supervisor's immediate superior or ethical board. It is suggested that this information be conveyed via a written report that is professional and succinct in nature.

It is extremely important to note that the student is accepting great responsibility by taking the second step above. In no way should this be done frivolously or with intent to harm. Doing so will only impede the student's progress both educationally and professionally.

INTERNSHIP CONSIDERATIONS

Continuing to take an active role in supervision applies also in your internship. The intern has a great responsibility to take initiative in choosing their internship setting and supervisor when at this pre-professional stage. Although you will ultimately choose your internship setting in conjunction with your faculty advisor, it is up to you narrow the field of possibilities through research and introspection regarding each internship site you are considering.

Choosing an internship site based purely on the population served or the locale could result in a strained supervisory relationship. Prior to deciding upon an internship, you should meet in person or on the telephone with your proposed supervisor and begin taking an active role in your internship by establishing rapport, exploring complementary viewpoints and discussing supervision styles.

Internships also provide unique opportunities for taking on responsibility in the supervisory process. For example, at this point the intern may wish to list their own goals for growth with timelines for reaching those goals. The intern may then go over these goals with the supervisor to determine appropriate means for reaching them as well as shifting goals as appropriate during the internship.

In this pre-professional stage, it is important to remember that there is still much to learn. The internship provides a place to exercise techniques and skills learned in fieldwork as well as a means through which to immerse yourself in new viewpoints and philosophies.

PROFESSIONAL CONSIDERATIONS

Once you have entered the professional world of music therapy, it might seem that the need for supervision has served its purpose. This is certainly not the case for the therapist who wishes to succeed and serve his/her clients well. As learning is a never-ending process that allows us to evolve not only in our chosen profession but also as individuals, supervision should be an ongoing part of the therapist's work. In your professional life, however, it may be difficult to find the supervision you need, especially if you are working as an independent contractor or as the sole music therapist in a facility. If you have worked to form support groups with peers during your college career and maintain appropriate relationships with your past supervisors, you are likely to have the necessary supervisory input and support to insure continued growth and development from other music therapists.

Becoming active in your national and regional music therapy associations is also of great help in this endeavor. Attendance at music therapy conferences allows you to touch base with past mentors and peers as well as participate in continuing education activities.

> Be open to learning through supervision throughout your career.

Remember, as well, that professionals from other fields have much valuable information to offer regarding client interaction, engagement and other therapeutic skills. Working as a team with other therapists can quickly forge a stimulating learning environment for everyone involved.

SUMMARY

Supervision is essential for growth as a student and as a music therapist. Some elements that contribute to a successful supervisory relationship include taking an active role in your supervision to establish rapport, assessing complementary viewpoints and identifying the appropriate supervisory style for your learning process. It is also important to utilize various forms of supervision, including live supervision, videotaped supervision and even self-critique and evaluation. Each of these modes provides a different viewpoint and experience of supervision. Taking a step-by-step approach to accepting feedback and criticism allows for increased objectivity and furthers one's ability to learn from the supervisory relationship. Learning from supervision is not only an essential part of the educational process, but also insures one's continued growth as a professional.

REFERENCES

Alley, J.M. (1980). The effect of self-analysis of videotapes on selected competencies of music therapy majors. *Journal of Music Therapy, 17,* 113-132.

American Music Therapy Association. (1998a). *AMTA code of ethics.* Silver Spring, NM.

Borczon, R.M. (1997). *Music Therapy: Group vignettes.* Gilsum, NH: Barcelona Publishers.

Bright, D. (1988). *Criticism in your life.* New York: Master Media Ltd.

Dileo, C. (2001). Ethical issues in Supervision. In Forinash, M. (2001). *Music therapy supervision* (pp. 19-38). Gilsum, NH: Barcelona Publishers.

Farnan, L.A. (1996). Issues in clinical training: The mystery of supervision. *Music Therapy Perspectives, 14,* 70-71.

Farnan, L.A. (1998). Issues in clinical training: Identifying and creating good interns – reader responses. *Music Therapy Perspectives, 16,* 60.

Feiner, S. (2001). A journey through internship supervision: Roles, dynamics and phases of the supervisory relationship. In Forinash, M. (2001). *Music therapy supervision* (pp. 99-115). Gilsum, NH: Barcelona Publishers.

Forinash, M. (2001). *Music therapy supervision*. Gilsum, NH: Barcelona Publishers.

Loganbill, C. Hardy, E. & Delworth, U. (1982). Supervision: A conceptual model. *The Counseling Psychologist, 10,* 3-42.

Madsen, C.K. & Kaiser, K.A. (1999). Pre-internship fears of music therapists. *Journal of Music Therapy, 36,* 17-25.

McClain, F.J. (2001). Music therapy supervision: A review of the literature. In Forinash, M. (2001). *Music therapy supervision* (pp. 9-17). Gilsum, NH: Barcelona Publishers.

Stoltenberg, C.D. & Delworth, U. (1987). *Supervising counselors and therapists; A developmental approach.* San Francisco, CA: Jossey-Bass Publishers.

Wheeler, B.L. (2000). Music therapy practicum practices: A survey of music therapy educators. *Journal of Music Therapy, 37,* 286-311.

Chapter 9

WHAT GOES AROUND ....

The purpose of this handbook is to offer practical information regarding aspects of the practice of music therapy. It is hoped that through this reading you will be better versed on how to become a stronger music therapist. While much of this book is drawn from over 25 years of my own experience as a music therapist, it also contains information written by music therapists I have known, taught, worked along side, and for whom I have great respect. In this final chapter, I expand the scope of this book to include the thoughts of many music therapists who offer various points of view about working in the world of music therapy. You will read words of advice drawn from experience with the hope that someday you will offer the same gift to those just beginning in the profession.

In the learning process, you will come across people who tell you things that help in your development as a music therapist. Many of these things you first heard in class from a professor, but for some reason you either did not absorb them or you may have forgotten the information. I can recall many instances of students returning to tell me: "I remember you saying this in class, but I just wasn't ready to hear it!" This chapter is a result of a mass email sent to many music therapists with varying years and levels of experience. I simply asked these professionals what information they might want to pass on to a less experienced music therapist embarking on the journey of professional life. I think the best way to read this chapter is very slowly, almost like an unfolding conversation over a cup of coffee. Some of these names are well known in the music therapy profession; others are hard working music therapists who are engaged daily in treating clients. These professionals have taken the time to think through their answers and respond to the question posed to them: "If you had the opportunity to pass on something to a developing music therapist, what would you say to him/her?"

WORDS OF EXPERIENCE

Your educational process is a time for growth, yet there cannot be growth without struggle. Use this time to stretch yourself and seek out challenges. Refuse to shy away from new experiences or unforeseen circumstances. Just as every response from a client is valid, every moment of your education provides the fuel for insight, creativity and leadership. Use this period, during which you have support as well as freedom, to explore and learn. Our common goal is to help others to achieve their fullest potential; it is up to you to determine how you may best serve that goal.

Holly Baxter, MT-BC

Music therapists need to remember to take care of themselves too. To feed themselves musically, have adequate support, and pay attention to their own physical, emotional, psychological, cognitive, spiritual and social needs in order to be fully prepared for their clients. Don't take on too much clinical work too soon! It is understandable to want to work with everyone, everyday, every hour but proceed steadily and build up your work gradually. You need to be passionate about this vocation - it is not "a job" but a lifelong journey during which you will discover as much about yourself as the clients you work with. Listen to your clients for they are your teachers. You will probably get to work with the clients you need to in order to be challenged and grow. Take full responsibility for the clinical situation. It is an honor to be involved with such unique and inspiring clients. Within them are encompassed the deepest, universal needs of humanity which inspire our commitment, care and actions. Be the best musician you possibly can to meet all your clients' needs! As an afterthought, I only recognized my mentors years after being a young student. I sailed through without really understanding the deeper implications of the work! So, I'd encourage students to keep hold of this book and refer to it regularly after graduating!

Julie Allis-Berghofer, RMT, MT(NR),PGCE

One of the most important things I learned in the development of my therapeutic style is how important it is to allow the relationship between myself and my client(s) to be the guiding force in each session. In other words, go into each session prepared with treatment plan, etc., but be present, open and sensitive to your client's needs and have the ability to switch gears if that is what is called for. Therefore, it is imperative that you have well developed music skills (guitar, voice, piano, improvisation, rhythmic instruments, etc.) readily available to "pull out of your bag" as the case may be. I have found that skill development happens as I do the work. It is important to keep practiced on whatever your instrument is, and continually expand your repertoire. However, my therapeutic style and method of playing change and grow as the process develops. Be patient, look for the small increments of change - perhaps the client is getting something out of the session(s) that you hadn't even planned on. As my mentor always said, be PRESENT at all times and willing to learn, change, be flexible and giving.
Renee Edwards, MT-BC

My teacher always mentioned to never burn your bridges. This is so true! Not only as professionals, but also as students. You never know when you will come across the path of another student sometime in your career. For example, an old classmate and I have been sharing an office for five months now. Not that we were ever on bad terms, but if we had a falling out at some time, it would be awkward to work together now.
Yael Klein, MT-BC

NETWORK, NETWORK, NETWORK! Pay attention to the people you meet at conferences and if they offer to help as a contact, take them up on it!
Jennifer Geiger, MT-BC

I am continually asked about starting a private practice and here is my typical response: A private practice should only be started after you have become proficient in working with a certain clientele. You should have some experience with politics, be great in charting and documentation, know the appropriate regulations, etc. and be financially stable. It takes at least a year of full time effort to build a private practice

and you should either have a spouse or family that can support you or have at least 6 months living expenses in the bank. If you do start a private practice, set your fees the same as Physical Therapists, Occupational Therapists, etc. in your area that perform services for the same clientele/population. Don't prostitute your profession. What you do is equally as valid! Whenever I get a new client who has a diagnosis that I am not familiar with, I go to the internet and research all I can about that condition. Knowing what "typical" is for a person with that diagnosis gives me a good starting point. When I get a client with a new self-stimulatory behavior that I am not familiar with, as long as the behavior is not self-injurious, I set a timer and spend at least 5 minutes straight engaging in that self-stimulatory behavior myself. Many times it gives me information about what sensory experience this behavior may fill for that child, and helps me to develop more appropriate replacement behaviors for that child. GO TO CONFERENCES!!! Both regional and national conferences are important to attend for so many reasons. First, you can gather new ideas and avoid burnout. Second, to get continuing education necessary to maintain your BC and broaden your scope as a professional. Third, to network and form a support group of professionals who do similar things as you do. And fourth, to help you get involved at some level in your professional association. Being involved in your association can be very rewarding; in fact, you may end up helping to form the future of your profession. Keep your membership in the American Music Therapy Association current as it gives you more credibility as a professional and can benefit you with journals, discounts on conferences, opportunities for volunteer involvement, mailings, and more. Live by the code of ethics of the AMTA and CBMT. They hold us accountable.
Lillieth Grand, MS, MT-BC

I'm thinking about how important it has been for me to have peer supervision and personal therapy. There's no reason to go out there on your own and lose the support that school afforded. The creative challenge, of course, is to create the support if it's not already established in your community. The first jobs have seemed more like a continuation of my training rather than the result of it. These would be the two most important aspects of my professional life that allow me to survive and at times thrive. Another really important thing is to keep (or return to)

playing music that nurtures YOU. Jam with people. Perform. Write. Do whatever you loved about music that made you want to be a music therapist in the first place. We often get so busy (and tired) from giving all the time and we forget (or neglect) to keep our creative reservoir full and abundant and flowing.
Kate Geller, MT-BC

The most important way to stay innovative and activated by your work is to do it for yourself at each and every juncture along the way. Through the years I have noticed a high burnout rate in music therapists who are not involved in their own music therapy process. No matter how many fabulous music experiences you have at your fingertips these experiences become stale quickly if you, as a therapist, do not have opportunities to partake in the music for yourself in a deep and meaningful way. In this philosophy the experience goes from the fingertips into the heart what is "out there" being provided by you as a therapist, must move "in here," meaning within your own heart and psyche. I avoid unhealthy use of countertransference by participating in my own music therapy and by working with a peer group of therapists (music, psychologists, social workers, dance therapists) who assist me in sorting out what my own experience is about. I use this group to re-ignite myself and to look at and value my own musical needs, powers, fears etc.
Dr. Joanne Loewy MT-BC

Things I have found (in)valuable along my path in music therapy: Learn. Be aware that we are all constantly gaining more knowledge, seasoned and unseasoned clinicians alike. Once the music therapy degree and certification are awarded, the learning continues indefinitely (or so we hope). Every interaction with a client, a caregiver, a parent, or a colleague is an opportunity to expand your mind, your experience and ultimately your skill as a clinician. It may not be textbook information that you gain, but if you are open and mindful you can catch a glimpse into the other person's experience, their opinions, their impressions of the world and even of you. Seek out learning opportunities, observe other therapists, find out about related fields, expand your scope. Find and learn about what else is out there and you will be closer to finding your place. Know that you will never know everything. Stay humble.

Talk with others about your experiences. Early professional and clinical experiences can be overwhelming and even embarrassing at times. This happens to us all. Practice humility and use the resources you have available to you. To move more quickly through these difficult early stages, it is going to be important to share your experience with others, seek out guidance and input - even if it is not from a music therapist! A counselor, social worker, psychiatric nurse or any other professional you feel comfortable talking to may very well have just the insights you need to inform your practice and get you through the tough stuff. They may not have THE answer, they may not have an answer at all. However, they have life experience, possibly clinical experience, or even experience from a completely unrelated professional field. If you do not receive supervision on the job, seek it out. Throughout your career you will find yourself searching for any number of answers to big questions. For this reason it is also beneficial to be in therapy yourself. We of all people should value the benefits of psychotherapy.
Gwendolyn Meier, MT-BC

As a mentor I would say trust yourself and what you have to offer your clients. Although your client may not be able to tell you or show you on his/her face, you may be the best thing that happens to them each day. Always evaluate your work. During sessions, be present for the client, but always ask yourself, "Why am I doing this song/activity/intervention..." There is always more to know, learn from other music therapists and professionals. Be prepared to answer the question, "What is music therapy?" everyday! Be an advocate for your own work. Get involved in conferences - present your ideas.
Kasi Peters, MT-BC

I think it's important to know that you really WILL spend the rest of your lives explaining your profession. So be prepared with a definition you can say in your sleep. If music therapy is new to the facility where you are hired you may be providing in-services to other employees of the company. Be prepared to do this well. This isn't a "traditional" field, and traditional types of jobs may be few and far between. Learn how to be assertive in the search for employment. If you want only to work with certain populations, you will probably have to CREATE yourself a job by pulling together a budget, research materials, plan of action, etc.

Learn who funds the music therapy program in your facility if it is funded by an outside source. Be aware that if you're working in a hospital and you're under the neuroscience department's financial umbrella, it's the neuroscience people you need to share research with, provide in-services for, etc. If you lose funding, it may be because you haven't proven the efficacy of your field. Make yourself available and responsible to your financial backer.
Penny Roberts, MT-BC

To survive as a new music therapist take the time to set up a solid support system, whether it is available through work, or outside of work. I've found that setting up a solid support system and utilizing those kinds of resources (i.e. own therapy, therapy groups, relaxation groups, or exercise class - something with structure that has a set time and place) has really helped me survive the stress of being a new professional and balancing "own time" versus "work time." I've also found this helpful in making me more aware of transference and/or counter-transference, since there is set time to reflect and to stop and ask myself, "Where am I with this?"
Nicole Tippets, MT-BC

I would like to share two things that have been very important in contributing to the richness of my experience as a music therapist. The first is to get to know other music therapists, and the second is to continue to grow as a music therapist.

We can enrich our lives as music therapists by getting to know other music therapists through friendships, networking, interactions with colleagues, and sharing our work. My relationships with other music therapists have been one of the most rewarding aspects of being a music therapist. Many of my friends are music therapists and I take advantage of and cultivate opportunities to get to know and exchange ideas with other music therapists. This means that, when I have a question about my clinical work or teaching or need some feedback on my writing, I have many people from whom I can get input. This enriches my experience and gives me easy access to feedback and the insights of others whom I respect. In addition, our profession is small enough and young enough that every music therapist can meet and learn from the leaders in music therapy. This provides a rare opportunity to learn from people who are at the forefront of the profession in which we are involved.

I also believe in the importance of continuing to grow as a music therapist. This has been a theme in my life and has meant that I am never bored or burned out. Some of this growth is through formal means such as going to school or attending workshops for continuing education credits. Some of the growth is through reading – there are many books and articles about music therapy and even more about the many fields to which music therapy is related. Some of my growth is through the informal contacts with music therapists spoken of in the previous paragraph, some may be through clinical supervision.

I grow when I investigate a new subject for a class that I am teaching or when I write an article or chapter. All of these are means of continuing my growth and I believe that it is through this continual growth that I have been able to be a good music therapist and also to maintain my enthusiasm for music therapy.

I hope that these suggestions are helpful. They are at the core of what has made my career as a music therapist meaningful and, I think, have also helped to make me a good music therapist.
Barbara Wheeler, MT-BC

Stay excited about music. Remember to have musical fun in your own life by playing, performing, and creating. It is all about the music – within the music you can unlock your dreams, dispel your fears, be in solitude or connect with the world. If it wasn't for the simple fact that music is what drew you into this glorious world of music therapy, you wouldn't be reading this now, nor would you have a song in the back of your mind just waiting to come out. Always come back to the music.
Ronald Borczon, MT-BC